Students' Guide to Information Technology

Books in the series

Students' Guide to Information Technology

Second Edition

Roger Carter

Reader in Information Technology, The Buckinghamshire College

BUTTERWORTH
HEINEMANN

Newnes
An imprint of Butterworth-Heinemann Ltd
Linacre House, Jordan Hill, Oxford OX2 8DP

 PART OF REED INTERNATIONAL BOOKS

OXFORD   LONDON   BOSTON
MUNICH   NEW DELHI   SINGAPORE   SYDNEY
TOKYO   TORONTO   WELLINGTON

First published 1989
Reprinted 1990
Second Edition 1993

British Library Cataloguing in Publication Data
Carter, Roger
    Students' Guide to Information
    Technology. – 2Rev.ed. – (Newnes
    Informatics Series)
    I. Title   II. Series
    004

ISBN 0 7506 0941 9

Library of Congress Cataloging in Publication Data
Carter, Roger, 1939–
    Students' guide to information technology/Roger Carter. – 2nd
    ed.
    p.   cm. – (The Newnes informatics series)
    Includes index.
    ISBN 0 7506 0941 9
    1. Information technology.   I. Title.   II. Series:
    Newnes informatics series.
    T58.5.C37   1993
    004–dc20   92–39699
                                                               CIP

Composition by Genesis Typesetting, Laser Quay, Rochester, Kent
Printed and bound in Great Britain by Biddles Ltd, Guildford and King's Lynn

Contents

Preface

Contents

guages – Systems software – Operating systems – How the operating system organizes the disk – Operating system commands – Operating environments – Windows – Using Windows – Other environments for PCs – Utilities – Application software – Features of application packages

Scenario – Technological covergence – Analogue and digital information – Audio and video systems – Technological convergence in audio systems – Technological convergence in video systems – Multimedia – Interactive video – Compact discs – Compact disc for multimedia applications – Data compression – Virtual reality systems

Scenario – What do we mean by communications? – How do electromagnetic communications work? – Technological convergence and communications – Fibre optics – The telecommunications problem – Carrier waves and modulation – Multiplexing – Modems – Communications systems and networks – Inter-computer communications – Local area networks – Circuit-switched networks – Packet-switched networks – the Open Systems Interconnection (OSI) reference model – Broadcast networks – Telecommunications services – On-line databases and bulletin boards – Electronic data interchange

Scenario – Introduction to information systems – The systems project life cycle – Systems analysis – The essential model – Reasons for using graphical modelling tools – The statement of purpose – The context diagram – The event list – Dataflow diagrams – The entity–relationship diagram – The data dictionary – Process specifications – Designing and implementing the system

Preface

The Butterworth-Heinemann Informatics series

This series of books from Butterworth-Heinemann gives up-to-date coverage of significant developments in information technology. Forthcoming titles investigate office automation, telecommunications, expert systems, computer-aided manufacture, and computer-based training, to name but a few topics.

The series is aimed at college students whose courses include IT components, including BTEC National and Higher Level courses, RSA and City & Guilds courses, as well as courses designed for the various professional bodies.

Traditionally, text books have adopted passive learning strategies, often being little more than back-up material for lectures. They make little attempt to help students either to check whether they have properly understood and digested the material they have read, or to put it into practice.

The books in this series mark a radical departure from this traditional approach. They adopt much more active strategies. Each chapter begins with a statement of what learning objectives the student is expected to achieve. At key points in the chapter the student is given the opportunity to achieve these objectives by carrying out short tasks. Feedback on the tasks is provided at the end of each chapter, so that the student can assess his or her learning, and as a further check a resumé of the chapter's contents is also given.

An important part of any course is assignment work, which both provides the student with additional practice and enables the tutor to carry out assessment of the student's progress. A key feature of the books in this series is their programme of assignments. Most chapters include an assignment with a distinctly practical flavour. The assignment may require the student to put learning into practice using a computer or other item of IT equipment, or it may require an in-depth investigation into a topic covered in the chapter.

Preface

Everyone involved in the preparation of this series

- the authors with expert knowledge of their subject who have invested so much of their time and effort in writing the material
- the educationalists at the IT Unit of the Buckinghamshire College who have checked it for clarity and educational relevance
- the publisher who has brought the series to fruition

believes that it will mark a significant step forward in the teaching and understanding of new technology.

The students' guide to information technology

This introductory book in the Butterworth-Heinemann Informatics series provides an overview of information technology. It includes an explanation of the microprocessor and the computer, an introduction to computer software, an account of audio and video technology, multimedia, and communications technology, and it gives the student an insight into office automation, into the use of IT in design and manufacturing, and into the design of information systems.

The emphasis throughout is on the practical value of the subject, and numerous tasks and assignments are given that enable the student to put into practice what he or she has learnt, often using a computer or other IT equipment.

In common with other books in the Butterworth-Heinemann Informatics series, each chapter begins with a statement of what the student is expected to achieve; the tasks in the chapter have been designed to enable the student to meet those objectives; and each chapter ends with feedback on the tasks so that he or she can check progress.

It is suitable for college students who are starting an information technology or computing course and who require a comprehensive introduction to the field, and for those for whom IT is one component of a more general business, technical, or professional course.

Roger Carter
The Information Technology Unit
The Buckinghamshire College

1: The information revolution

Objectives

After reading this chapter, you should be able to:
- say what is meant by *information*, and describe the main kinds of information that we use
- define *information technology* and identify the main techniques and devices that it involves
- outline the main ways in which information technology is revolutionizing society, business, and our private lives.

Scenario

Imagine you are a youth club leader, and that one of your current tasks is to organize the summer camp. Life under canvas might seem a world away from information technology and computers, but as you will learn in this chapter, information technology affects every part of our lives. It can have as big an impact on your summer camp as on the world of the office and factory.

What is information?

Being the camp organizer involves you in many things: selling the idea of a summer camp to the club members, picking a site for the camp, taking bookings, hiring tents, organizing helpers and delegating duties, arranging transport, and so on.

One thing you must do, of course, is to tell everyone – in particular the drivers – how to get to the site. There are four ways in which you might do this:

1 give the Ordnance Survey map reference of the site
2 type out and photocopy a description of the route, containing road numbers, towns, and other directions for reaching the site

3 draw a road map to the site and photocopy this
4 give a verbal description of the route to the site.

Although these are quite different methods, each with its advantages and disadvantages, they all contain *information* on how to reach the site.
Read this list again, and see if you can decide what is meant by the term information.
Here are two possible definitions:

1 facts and ideas presented in a meaningful form
2 a representation or *model* of some aspect of the real world.

In the camp site example, the aspect of the world under consideration is the route to the site, and the facts being represented are a sequence of landmarks and roads.

Four kinds of information

The four methods listed above are presenting the same information – how to get to the site – in different forms. These different forms of information are as follows.

1 Data

The first method presents the information in its barest and most elementary form, as a string of characters (letters and numbers). We call this *data*, and an item of data may be a name, a price, a quantity, a code number, or, as in this case, a map reference.

By itself, an item of data is not much use. It is only when it is combined with other information – in this case the information contained on an Ordnance Survey map – that it becomes meaningful and useful.

2 Text

The second method presents the information written as phrases and sentences. We call this *text*. Although much longer than a bare item of data, it is much more meaningful, and in this case forms a complete guide to reaching the site.

2

3 Image

The third method presents the information in pictorial form. This includes charts, graphs, and, as in this case, freehand drawings. We call this *image*. Again, information in this form is more comprehensive than an item of data, and more meaningful.

4 Voice

The fourth method presents the information in spoken phrases and sentences. We call this *voice*. Like text, it is much more meaningful than an item of data.

Often, we use two or more of these forms of information to convey a message. As camp organizer, you could use all four to make sure that everyone reaches the site: you might draw a map, with the Ordnance Survey reference and a written route included on it, and you might back this up with a verbal explanation.

Sometimes you have to choose between alternative methods of presenting the same information. You should select the method which most clearly and accurately represents the aspect of the real world you are seeking to convey.

Questions

1 If you had to choose just one of these four ways of giving directions to the site, which would you choose and why?
2 List four methods by which information on stock market movements is conveyed to the general public.

Information processing

My answer to the first question above would be method 3, i.e. to give the information in the form of a route map. I would choose this because, in my opinion, it gives the clearest and most realistic representation of the route.

Can you recall the difference between method 1 (the Ordnance Survey map reference) and the other three methods? It is the only method of the four in which the information is given in the form of an item of data which, in the absence of other information, is quite meaningless. If as camp leader you were given this item of data – perhaps over the phone – you would have to do quite a bit of work to produce from it some meaningful information such as a route map.

Here's the sequence of tasks you would have to carry out:

1 *capture* the data which gives the location of the camp site, i.e. obtain the map reference over the phone
2 *store* the data by jotting it down on paper, and *retrieve* it later on
3 *process* the data, firstly by relating it to other information (i.e. data contained on the Ordnance Survey map), then performing calculations perhaps with a calculator to work out distances, and producing from it your own route map
4 *communicate* this route map to other people by photocopying it and passing copies to them.

Whenever we provide people with useful information from information held in other forms, we have to go through this sequence of tasks. The term *information processing*, while applying particularly to task 3, is often used in a general way to refer to the entire capture-store-process-communicate sequence.

Questions

3 List the information processing sequence your tutor has to go through to produce your final coursework grade at the end of the year.
4 In the information processing sequence listed above, what information handling devices are (or might be) used to assist the production of a route map?

What is information technology?

How did you do in Question 4? Here's the list of information handling devices I drew up in my answer:

● the telephone (to capture the data)
● pencil and paper (to store the data and to produce the map)
● a calculator (to add up distances)
● a photocopier (to copy the route map).

This list is a mixture of old-fashioned devices (the pencil) and modern devices (such as the calculator). If I asked you to say which of these were *information technology* (IT) devices, you would probably feel that the pencil at least should be excluded, as it is something we associate with pre-IT days. And you would be quite right to exclude it – most of what we mean by IT comes from the world of electronics, and includes in particular computing and telecommunications devices (such as the calculator and the telephone).

Here, then, is a definition of information technology that encapsulates what we've said so far:

> Information technology (IT for short) is the use of modern technology to aid the capture, storage, retrieval, analysis, and communication of information, whether in the form of data, text, image, or voice.

Note the reference to 'modern' technology in this definition. Traditional methods of information handling using simple tools such as pencils are excluded. Most IT devices are controlled by microprocessors (see Chapter 2), and these may be incorporated into the equipment itself (as in the case of telephones that offer autodial facilities), or in the computers that control the equipment.

Physically, a microprocessor is a tiny sliver of silicon, usually packaged in a holder which contains the electrical connections needed to link it to other devices. Figure 1.1 shows a packaged silicon chip.

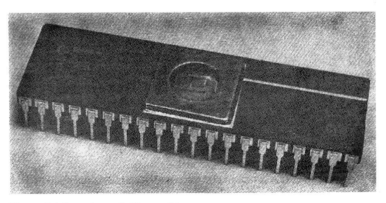

Figure 1.1 A packaged silicon chip

IT devices

In order to give you an idea of the scope of IT, here's a more comprehensive list of IT devices. For convenience, I have grouped them according to the main information processing task that they perform, i.e. capture, store, process, or communicate. Don't worry if you are unsure of some of the terms used here, as all these devices will be explained in full in later pages.

Capture

- keyboards – for keying in data or text to a computer
- computer mice – for drawing with a computer
- microphones – for speech and music input to computer, audio, or telecommunications
- video cameras and scanners – for video and graphics input to computer, video, and telecommunications systems

Storage

- memory chips – for short-term storage of data in computer systems
- magnetic disks and disk-drives – for long-term storage of data in computer systems
- magnetic tape and tape-drives – for long-term storage of data in computer systems, speech or music in audio systems, and image in video systems
- compact discs and players – for long-term storage of data in computer systems, and speech and music in audio systems, and image in video systems
- video discs and players – for storage of speech, music, and image in video and computer systems

Processing

- logic chips – for analysing data in computer and other electronic systems
- mixing and editing consoles – for processing sound and image information in audio and video systems
- message switching and routeing devices – for telecommunications systems

Communications

- monitors – for displaying the output of computer and video systems
- printers – for producing a permanent copy of output from computer systems
- loudspeakers – for reproducing the output from audio systems
- wires, optic fibres, and broadcast devices – for use in telecommunications systems.

The IT revolution

The growth in electronics over the past quarter century has been phenomenal. What we have seen is not an evolution in technology, but a revolution. Our society, our businesses, our homes, and our leisure activities, are being transformed.

Modern electronics is based upon the *microprocessor*, one form of *microchip*, which consists of miniature logic circuits etched onto the surface of a sliver of silicon. These tiny circuits replace the enormous banks of glass valves used in the earliest computers of the 1940s and 1950s.

Another form of microchip is the *memory chip*, used to store information. Nowadays, the main parts of a computer – the memory and the logic – can be held on a single chip, though to form a usable system a keyboard, monitor, and disk-drive must be attached. Where memory and logic are situated on one chip, the chip is officially known as a *microcomputer*, although the term has become misused to mean any computer with a microprocessor at its heart.

The early computers processed information in the form of data. Modern computers are more powerful, and can handle information in other forms, including graphics and speech. However, they work on the same principles as the early models, which are explained in the next chapter. The main difference between the computers of 30 years ago and the microchips of today lies in the fact that the latter are very small, very cheap, very reliable, and very powerful. In fact, ever since the first chips were made in the early 1960s, their power has increased every year while their cost has decreased. It is this fact, continued over a quarter of a century, that has caused the information revolution.

Microprocessors are now incorporated not just into computers, but into a wide range of other products, from cameras to washing machines and cars. But what has an information processing device to do with a camera, washing machine, or car? The answer is that the microprocessor is used as a control mechnism in many of these products. This means that it makes adjustments on the basis of information received, perhaps on the product's performance or on its environment. In the case of a camera, for example, this means processing information such as the intensity of the light in order to adjust the lens aperture and other settings.

Question

5 Spend a couple of minutes jotting down all the products containing microprocessors that you think might be taken to the summer camp.

The impact of the IT revolution

Microprocessors are now so cheap and so small that they can be incorporated into any device that can benefit from the power of the computer. What this means is that, to an increasing extent, appliances are able to control themselves, so that the minimum of human intervention is required. This has had an obvious impact on our lives, for it has brought in its wake enormous improvements in efficiency and productivity, as well as affecting our patterns of work and our leisure.

The remarkable developments in recent years of audio and video systems and broadcasting have also contributed significantly to the IT revolution, and these too have had a major impact on our lives.

Here, in brief, is how the IT revolution is affecting all aspects of our lives.

The home

Radio and TV broadcasting, Prestel, Ceefax, and Oracle, and home video and audio systems, have had an obvious impact on our home lives. Washing machines, microwave ovens, cookers, indeed every kind of appliance are controlled by microprocessors. Modern telephones, TVs, and cameras all depend upon them. Quite new kinds of products, which would not have been possible without the microprocessor, are now commonplace – such as the digital watch, video games, the electronic musical keyboard, and the home computer.

The office

Modern photocopiers, calculators, and typewriters are controlled by microprocessors. Most important of all, of course, is the computer, by which so many office jobs are now done, from writing letters and reports to keeping records, producing charts and graphs, and controlling projects.

The factory

Nowadays, products are designed by computer, using computer-aided design techniques. In the factory where the products are made, the equipment and processes are often controlled by microchips, including the machine tools, assembly lines, and industrial robots. Even warehousing of the finished products is often computer-controlled.

Transport and communications

Cars, fax machines, and the telephone network, are some of the devices and systems which are now controlled by microprocessors. The railways and underground systems are also increasingly computer-controlled, and computer-based telecommunications systems are now widely used.

Society

In education, the microprocessor is playing an increasing role. Computer-based learning materials, including video material stored on video disc or video tape, are growing in popularity, and computers and educational software are widely used in schools and colleges. In retailing, microprocessor-based point-of-sale systems are common-place, and links are being established between these and the banking system, so that goods can be purchased by directly debiting the customer's account. In law enforcement, computer databases are being used to increase police efficiency in fighting crime. One of the biggest users of microprocessors is now the military, with its computerized battle-management systems, guided missiles, and other hardware.

IT and employment

The IT revolution is just the latest in a long line of technological revolutions: the Stone Age, the Bronze Age, the Iron Age, and so on. All these technological advances have had two main effects upon employment:

● They have altered the pattern of employment, as old skills and jobs become obsolete and new ones emerge. During this transition period, inevitable social dislocations arise.

● They have resulted in increased productivity, so that more is produced from the same amount of labour. This has led to increased wealth, and to the ability of society to support jobs that are not concerned with the direct production of food and other material products, and also to increased leisure. The increased leisure may manifest itself as shorter working hours, or as actual unemployment.

The technological advances that have occurred in the last couple of centuries (i.e. since the start of the Industrial Revolution) differ from earlier advances in two important respects:

● They have happened very rapidly, so that the social dislocations caused by them have been more acute. Large numbers of people can be thrown out of work in the space of only a few years. And people with jobs may need significant amounts of retraining several times in their working lives.

● They have involved a heavy investment in manufacturing plant. This led, in the initial phase of each advance, to a significant increase in employment.

The current technological advance is centred on the widespread incorporation of the microchip into manufacturing plant and manufactured products. The various elements needed to implement computer-integrated manufacturing are appearing – robots, automatic materials handling, and so on (see Chapter 9). The investment that is being made in this technology should result in a significant short-term increase in both output and employment in the industrialized world as new kinds of machines and new kinds of factories are developed and constructed. The long-term effects may, however, be static or declining employment.

One of the accompaniments to technological advance is changing employment patterns and the need for new skills. This is manifesting itself at present by the concern being expressed in many industries throughout much of the developed world at the shortage of suitably trained and skilled labour.

IT and employment patterns

As I've said, one of the effects of technological advance is increased productivity and greater wealth. This reduces the labour required for the production of food and other basic economic tasks, and increases the ability of society to sustain other types of jobs. So, over the centuries, we have seen a steady movement of labour away from agriculture, mining, and other 'primary' industries, through 'secondary' (i.e. manufacturing) industries, and into the 'tertiary' (service industry) sector of the economy.

● A few centuries ago most of the labour force worked in the primary sector, on the land. Today, the figure is one or two per cent.
● A few decades ago, most of the labour force was employed in manufacturing.
● Today, most of the labour force works in service industries.

This steady movement in the pattern of employment is likely to continue, and even accelerate with the introduction of computer-integrated manufacturing. It may be that in two decades from now manufacturing employment will fall to the kinds of levels that we associate with farming, with perhaps 95% of jobs being in the service sector of the economy. Many people in the service sector are 'information' workers, using IT equipment such as computers.

One of the features that characterized the Industrial Revolution was the concentration of manufacturing in factories with expensive large-scale plant and production lines. So there was a mass movement of people away from the countryside into the towns and cities where the factories were concentrated. Although the Industrial Revolution ultimately raised living standards enormously, this mass migration to urban areas lowered the quality of many aspects of people's lives

In contrast to this, the information technology revolution is characterized by the miniaturization of computer components and the development of communications networks. As a result, the need for information workers to travel to work in large city offices is reduced. Many jobs can be done in remote locations, linked electronically to the central site. Many companies have moved their offices away from congested centres of population, and a number of individuals now carry out a significant part of their work on personal computers at home, able to communicate with their organization's central computer via the telephone network. This reverses many of the negative influences of the Industrial Revolution, leading to improvements in the quality of life.

Assignment 1

Choose an activity in your home, work, or leisure life, such as photography, cooking, or cars, and investigate the ways in which it is being affected by the use of microprocessors. Write up the results of your investigation in the form of a report, in which you:

a describe how microprocessors are used in this activity

b outline the advantages that have resulted from the use of microprocessors in this activity, and the disadvantages (if any).

Recap

● *Information* is facts and ideas presented in a meaningful form, normally as data, text, image, or voice.

● *Information processing* refers to the sequence of tasks you have to perform to produce information:

1 capture the facts

2 store them

3 process them

4 communicate the results of the processing.

● *Information technology* is the use of technology to perform these information processing tasks. IT devices exist to assist each of the four information processing tasks. Computer systems, telecommunications systems, audio and video systems, and modern control systems are all part of IT.

● The IT revolution is founded on the *microprocessor*, which can be used for storing and processing information. Today, microprocessors are used to control every type of appliance and industrial process, and they lie at the heart of modern computers.

● IT can give enormous increases in productivity. This means that the same amount of labour will produce a much greater amount of wealth. If other restrictions exist on the amount of wealth that is able to be created – such as depletion of resources or the inability of society to absorb the increased wealth – then unemployment will result.

Answers to questions

1 Image (possibly), because a drawing gives the clearest and most realistic model of the information (i.e. the route).
2 a data, e.g. FT index
  b written report, e.g. in press
  c chart of movements, e.g. on TV
  d verbal report, e.g. over the radio.
3 a mark and grade assignments
  b record (i.e. store) grades
  c calculate overall grade
  d communicate this grade in a report.
4 Telephone, pencil and paper, ruler, calculator, photocopier.
5 A few are: cars, digital watches, cameras, calculators, audio and video equipment, electronic games.

2: Computers

Objectives

After reading this chapter, you should be able to:
- define what is meant by the term *computer* and outline its main components
- describe the main function of a microprocessor and explain in outline how it works
- define the meaning of *binary digit* and explain why modern IT equipment handles information in binary digital form
- list the main types of microprocessor used in computers, and give their relative advantages and disadvantages
- outline the main types of computer memory
- classify computers into their various types.

Scenario

As the youth club leader in charge of the summer camp, you have many administrative tasks to perform. You may also have artwork to produce. You wish to automate as many of these tasks as possible, using a computer. But which computer should you buy?

What is a computer?

A computer is a device which enables you to process information (1) automatically and (2) in accordance with instructions that you give it. (1) means that it can carry out the capture–store–process–communicate sequence described in Chapter 1 all by itself, or at least with the minimum of human intervention. It does this by means of *hardware*, i.e. information capture, processing, storage, and communicating devices, linked together electronically. (2) means that it can be adapted to carry out almost any kind of information processing task, whether word processing or stock control. It does this by means of *software,* i.e. sets of instructions or *programs* which control these hardware devices so that they carry out the required operations on the information.

In this chapter and the next we look at the various pieces of hardware. In Chapter 4 we turn our attention to the software.

Question

1 A low-cost pocket calculator has a number of features in common with a computer, but one essential difference. From what has been said above, what are these similarities and differences?

Computer hardware

The hardware of a computer system consists of the devices listed below. They are all described in this chapter and the next.

- Input devices to capture the information, such as the keyboard, mouse, microphone, or scanner.

- The central processing unit (CPU), containing the *arithmetic logic unit* (ALU), which carries out the logical and arithemetic computations that lie at the heart of computing (see below), and the *control unit*, which executes commands typed at the keyboard or stored in software.

- Storage is split into short-term *memory*, using microchips inside the computer, which hold data and programs while processing is being carried out, and long-term *storage*, normally using magnetic disks.

- Output devices for communicating the results of the processing, such as a printer, monitor, or loudspeaker.

- I should also mention the circuitry linking these various devices, consisting of eight, 16, or 32 strands of parallel wire, called *buses*, along which all the bits that make up each item of the information travel in parallel.

One way of representing a computer system is by the set of input–storage–processing–output boxes shown in Figure 2.1. The arrows linking the boxes indicate the flow of data through the system.

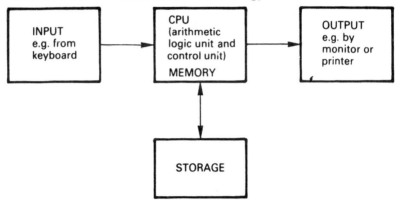

Figure 2.1 A computer system

Microprocessors

I'll start by describing microprocessors (microchips), as these lie at the heart of computers and other information processing devices. The CPU inside a modern computer will consist of one or more of these chips, which contain the logic circuitry needed to perform computations. A chip is packaged in a holder containing the electrical connections needed to link it to other devices such as keyboard (see Figure 1.1). Microchips which act as memory are described later in this chapter.

In essence, a microprocessor works in the same way as the roomsful of glass valves that made up the guts of the earliest computers. Each valve formed a switch which could be turned OFF by applying a strong negative electrical charge to it, or ON by applying a weak electrical charge. If it was ON a current could flow through it, if it was OFF no current could flow.

Instead of valves, which were bulky, unreliable, and expensive, we now have an alternative type of electrically operated switch, the tiny transistor. A transistor is shown in diagrammatic form in Figure 2.2.

A transistor consists of three layers of doped silicon, i.e. silicon to which a small amount of another substance has been added. Doped silicon is a semiconductor: under certain circumstances it will conduct electricity, but under other circumstances it won't. Silicon can be positively doped, i.e. the added substance has fewer valence electrons than pure silicon, or negatively doped, i.e. the added substance has an excess of valence electrons. In either case, electric current can flow under the right conditions.

A strong charge applied to the central positively doped layer in the transistor allows a current to flow between the two negatively doped

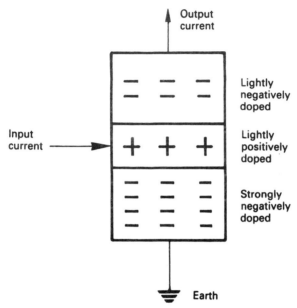

Figure 2.2 A transistor

layers, but if there is no charge or if it is weak then it will prevent its flow. In this way the transistor acts like a switch, allowing current to flow or not flow between the two negative layers.

A microprocessor is made up of many thousands of transistors, linked to each other by microscopic circuitry etched into the surface of the chip.

How a microprocessor handles information

Valves and transistors operating in this way can be thought of as *bistable* devices, because they are in only one of two states, in this case

17

either OFF or ON. Other devices used in computers and other IT equipment are also bistable. For example:

● a spot on the surface of storage devices such as magnetic disks or tape can be either magnetized or demagnetized
● a hole position on paper tape can be either punched or not punched
● a spot on the surface of an optical compact disc can either have a pit burnt in it or not.

This means that these devices have to store information as sequences of ON/OFF switches, or sequences of magnetized/demagnetized spots, or sequences of holes/no-holes. If we call an ON switch (or a magnetized spot, or a hole) *1*, and if we call an OFF switch (or a demagnetized spot, or a no-hole) *0*, then all information must be broken down into sequences of 1s and 0s to be handled by a computer or other microprocessor-based equipment.

For example, when you type the letter *A* on a computer keyboard, it is converted to the following sequence of 0s and 1s:
01000001
The letter *B* is converted to 01000010, the letter *C* to 01000011, the letter *D* to 01000100, and so on.

To reach the CPU, a 1 becomes a strong pulse of electricity travelling down the wire linking the keyboard to the computer, and a 0 becomes a weak pulse.

When they reach the CPU microprocessor inside the computer, each weak pulse switches a transistor OFF, while a strong pulse turns a transistor ON. In this way a letter pressed on the keyboard is converted to an ON/OFF switch sequence inside the computer.

Pocket calculators work in a similar way, as does every other microprocessor-based device. When you draw a picture on the computer screen, using drawing software, the computer converts your artistry into sequences of 0s and 1s which give screen co-ordinates, colours, and other information about each point of your picture. If you speak into a speech recognition device, your words are converted into sequences of 0s and 1s which correspond to tone, amplitude, and other vocal characteristics.

These 0s and 1s are numerical *digits*. Devices such as computers which convert information to this form are said to be *digital*. In the past, some computers were not digital, but instead represented data as varying voltages. These were called *analogue* computers. Modern microprocessors are so cheap and so powerful that almost all IT devices are now digital.

Question

2 Look at what I said above about the computer's representation of A, B, C, and D. What sequence of switches do you think is used to store the letter E?

Binary numbers

Each of these sequences of 0s and 1s is an item of numerical data. It is because computers reduce all information to data in this form that the term *data processing* is normally applied to them, rather than *information processing*.

You have probably met numbers that use just the two digits 0 and 1 in your school maths. They are called *binary numbers*. They relate to our ordinary decimal numbers as follows:

Decimal	Binary
zero	0
one	1
two	10
three	11
four	100
five	101

and so on. Can you discern the pattern in this?

The digits 0 and 1 that make up a binary number are called binary digits, or *bits* for short. In most computers, information is handled in groups of eight bits, which is why there are eight 0s and 1s in the binary representations of A, B, C, and D above. A group of eight bits is called a *byte*, which may be short for 'by eight'.

As I said earlier, microprocessors contain many thousands of transistors (switches), and magnetic disks and other IT equipment also contain huge numbers of bistable devices. To cope with quantities of this magnitude we usually talk of:

● Kb or Kbyte (short for *kilobyte*), meaning about 1,000 bytes (1024, to be exact)
● Mb or Mbyte (short for megabyte), meaning about 1,000,000 bytes (1024 Kb, to be exact)
● Gb or Gbyte (short for gigabyte), meaning 1,000,000,000 bytes (1024 Mb, to be exact).

Microprocessors and logic

Microprocessors are sometimes called logic chips, because they work according to the rules of logic. The earliest computers also worked according to these rules. The glass valves in those computers, and the transistor switches in modern microprocessors, are organized into what are called *logic gates*. These enable the microprocessor to carry out the logical operations AND, OR, and NOT. The significance of this is that by combining these operations, the microprocessor can perform arithmetic and other tasks on the information that is fed into it.

So to explain how microprocessors compute, we need briefly to look at the rules governing logical operators. They come from Boolean algebra, a branch of mathematics developed by Boole in the early part of the last century. These rules go something like this.

Any proposition can be true or false. For example, the proposition *Ann is going on the summer camp* is either true or false, as is the proposition *Barbara is going on the summer camp*. We'll call the first proposition A and the second B. We'll also use the number 1 to represent true and the number 0 to represent false. So in the language of Boolean algebra,

A = 1 means: *Ann is going to the camp* is true
A = 0 means: *Ann is going to the camp* is false

Similarly,

B = 1 means: *Barbara is going to the camp* is true
B = 0 means: *Barbara is going to the camp* is false

We can combine the propositions A and B using the logical operators AND, OR and NOT.

The AND operator

Using the above camping example,

A AND B = 1 means: *Ann is going* and *Barbara is going* are both true
A AND B = 0 means: *Ann is going* and *Barbara is going* are not both true, i.e. either one or the other, or both, are false.

We can represent statements like this by a *truth table*. A truth table for this example shows the effect of different values of A and B on the value taken by A and B:

A	B	A AND B
0	0	0
0	1	0
1	0	0
1	1	1

The first line of this table means:

If *Ann is going* is false, and if *Barbara is going* is false, then *Ann and Barbara are going* is false.

Question

3 Is the above table correct? Check this by thinking about what each line of it means.

The AND gate

Figure 2.3 shows an AND gate. This is an electrical circuit which performs the AND operations described below. In its original form (before the days of microchips), the switches at A and B were mechanical devices called solenoids. An electrical current in wire A

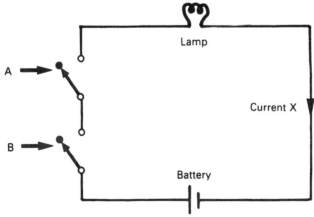

Figure 2.3 An AND gate

closed the switch at A, and an electrical current in wire B closed the switch at B. In order to complete the circuit and allow the current marked X to flow from the battery through the lamp, both switches had to be closed, i.e. there had to be a current in wire A and in wire B. If either one of these wires had no current flowing in it, then one of the switches would be open and no current would flow.

Using 1 to represent the flow of current and 0 to represent the absence of current, we can draw up the following truth table showing the values of X for different values of A and B:

A	B	X
0	0	0
0	1	0
1	0	0
1	1	1

This is exactly the same as the truth table for the AND operator given above, and means that this circuit correctly represents the action of that operator.

In modern computers, tiny transistors in the CPU replace the two solenoid-operated switches.

The OR operator

The second logical operator is OR, which is used like this:

A OR B = 1 means: *Ann is going* is true, or *Barbara is going* is true, or both are true

A OR B = 0 means: none of the above are true, i.e. both propositions are false.

Again, we can draw up a truth table to represent this:

A	B	A OR B
0	0	0
0	1	1
1	0	1
1	1	1

Question

4 Is the above table correct? Check by thinking about what each line of this truth table means.

The electrical circuit shown in Figure 2.4 is able to reproduce the effect of this table. In this, the switches A and B are in parallel, and current X will flow if either A or B (or both) are closed.

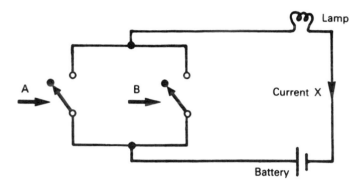

Figure 2.4 An OR gate

The NOT operator

The third logical operator is NOT. NOT A means *Ann is not going* and NOT B means *Barbara is not going*. So if *Ann is going* is true, then NOT A is false. The truth table representing this is:

A	NOT A
0	1
1	0

In electronics, a NOT gate consists of a special sort of switch which closes and so makes a circuit when no current is applied to it, and opens and so breaks the circuit when there is a current.

23

Combining logical operators

We can combine these logical operators (and the circuits which represent them) in any number of ways. For example, Colin may decide to go to the camp if:

(A OR B) AND NOT (A AND B) = 1

This means that he will go to the camp if

A OR B = 1, i.e. Ann or Barbara go

AND if

NOT (A AND B) = 1, i.e. if they don't both go.

So he'll go with one or the other but not both!

The truth table for this can be built up in stages. The first stage is to construct the value for A OR B and NOT (A AND B). The second stage combines these two first-stage results using the AND operator. Here's the first two lines of this table:

A	B	A OR B	NOT (A and B)	(A OR B) AND NOT (A AND B)
0	0	0	1	0
0	1	1	1	1

Question

5 Try producing the last two lines of the above truth table.

Arithmetic and logic gates

Most of the work done by a computer involves arithmetic calculations. The basic task in arithmetic is the addition of two binary numbers. Here's a table showing the values of A + B for all the possible values of A and B:

A	B	A + B	Explanation
0	0	0	Zero + zero = zero
0	1	1	Zero + one = one
1	0	1	One + zero = one
1	1	10	One + one = two (i.e. 10 in binary)

From your work with binary numbers at school, you probably know that the last column of this table, which shows the results of the addition, really consists of two columns: a twos column (i.e. 10 in binary) and a units column. So we could rewrite the above table like this:

A	B	A + B	
		2's	1's
0	0	0	0
0	1	0	1
1	0	0	1
1	1	1	0

Notice that the two's column is identical to the results column of the A AND B truth table in the last section. The one's column is the same as the results column of the (A OR B) AND NOT (A AND B) table in the last section. This means that we can use logical operators (and hence logic gates) to reproduce these two columns, and therefore to carry out binary calculations.

Logic circuits

The AND, OR, and NOT gates used in logic chips are represented by the special symbols shown in Figure 2.5. These symbols can be combined to show more complex gate circuits, and Figure 2.6 shows the circuit needed to carry out binary addition. It consists of a combination of an AND gate (to give the two's column) and an (A OR B) AND NOT (A AND B) gate system (to give the one's column). This circuit is known as a *half-adder gate*.

Although there are many different kinds of microprocessor, they all consist of various arrangements of logic gates, such as the one shown

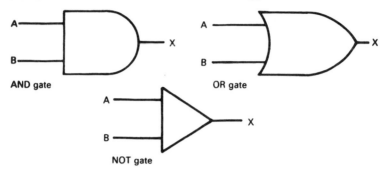

Figure 2.5 Symbols used for AND, OR and NOT gates

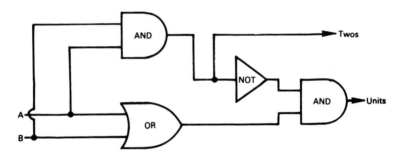

Figure 2.6 A half-adder gate

above. It is circuits like these that enable chips to perform calculations and therefore to be used in calculators, cars, cameras, and computers.

Microprocessors and computers

Any suitable type of switch can be used to build up the logic gate circuits used in the central processing units (CPUs) of computers. However, because many thousands are required to construct circuits for even the simplest computer, it is important that they should be small, reliable, cheap, and consume little power. Back in the 1940s and 1950s, there were very few computers, and those that existed were very large, expensive, and unreliable. This was because glass valves were used as switches inside their CPUs. The development of the transistor, used in today's microprocessors, brought about the revolution in switches inside their CPUs. The development of the transistor, used in today's microprocessors, brought about the revolution in switch technology needed for the spread of computing.

In the future, other types of switching device may prove viable. Some researchers are currently working on optical computers, using pulses of laser light instead of pulses of electrons to communicate the 0s and 1s of binary code. By constructing optical AND, OR, and NOT gates they have demonstrated the feasibility of such computers. Their potential advantages are apparent when you consider that:

● no electrical wires will be needed, which will reduce the cost
● Their speed will surpass that of electronic computers, as the information will travel at the speed of light.

However, optical computers have a long way to go to catch up with the high-volume and low-cost production of microprocessors, and the present-day type of computer, using microprocessors as CPUs, will certainly reign supreme up to the end of this century.

There are a number of different microprocessor designs ('architectures') used for computer CPUs. Some, such as the Motorola 68000 series of microchips, contain an arrangement of logic circuits more suited for graphical applications, and so are used on the Apple Macintosh, the Atari ST, and the Amiga computers. Others, such as the Intel 80 × 86 series of chips, are more suitable for processing numerical data and text, and are used on the successors to the original IBM PC. Having said that, the latest generations of such chips are so powerful that there is little practical difference in their respective abilities to handle graphical or numerical applications, and the Apple Macintosh and the IBM PC's successors now run very similar software. If a software package proves a major success on one system, it's not long before it is converted to run on the other.

The most popular makes of CPU chips are described in the sections below. Each new generation may contain several times as many transistors as its predecessors, indicative of the fact that it has a greater number of and more complex logic circuits. Among other things, these enable it to:

● carry out operations at higher speeds

● perform calculations to more significant figures (i.e. a higher degree of accuracy)
● directly address more memory (and therefore support more complex software).

An important factor which affects all these is the number of bits that the CPU is able to process simultaneously. In the 1970s, the standard was 8-bit CPUs, whereas today it is 32-bits. This implies not only many more transistors in today's microprocessors, but also many more parallel wires in the data buses (cables) inside the computer. To keep costs down, some computers contain 32-bit chips but 16-bit data buses, i.e. the chips process data 32 bits at a time, but communicate data only 16 bits at a time.

The Z80 microprocessor

This microchip, manufactured by Zilog, was the main CPU used in microcomputers in the 1970s and early 1980s. It is still used today in some low-priced computers such as the Amstrad PCW word processor. An enormous amount of business software has been written for computers which use this chip, and much of it is very cheap or even free.

The Z80 is, however, an 8-bit chip, and therefore of limited power. It is slow, and able to access only 64 Kbytes of memory. The result is that software running on Z80-based computers is no match for the kind of thing that is now available on more up-to-date machines.

The 680 × 0 family of microprocessors

These are 32 bit microprocessors from Motorola. They appeared in the mid-1980s, and are used on computers which are strong on graphics such as the Apple Macintosh, and Atari ST, and the Amiga. The original chip, used on the first Apple Mac, was the 68000, the latest model (at the time of writing) is the 68040. These chips are fast, and able to access many gigabytes of memory.

The 80 × 86 family of microprocessors

These microprocessors, from Intel, are the most widely used, being the ones adopted by the IBM PC and its successors. 'Clones' of these chips are also available from other manufacturers. Most PCs today, whether 'compatibles' from the likes of Toshiba, Tandon, Olivetti, and Amstrad, or PS/2 machines from IBM itself, use these chips. In future I shall use the term 'PC' to mean personal computers of this type, as distinct from other microcomputers such as the Apple Macintosh.

The 8086 chip, used on earlier models of the IBM PC (at the beginning of the 1980s), was a 16-bit chip. It was therefore faster than the Z80 (which it effectively replaced), and could access 640K of memory. When the IBM PC first appeared, all business software on microcomputers was designed to run within 64K, and the potential to access ten times this amount seemed more than generous. Today, it seems paltry.

In the mid-1980s IBM produced a more advanced version of the PC called the AT. This boasted the latest 32-bit 80286 chip which was capable, in theory, of accessing many Megabytes of memory (32 Mb in fact). Unfortunately, the operating system used on PCs limited it to 640K (see Chapter 4), and in any case the chip itself turned out to be 'brain damaged' and not capable of fulfilling these expectations. Today, the much more powerful 80386 and 80486 chips are with us, with none of these memory limitations. At the time of writing the operating system still restricts memory access, but operating environments such as Windows break the 640K memory barrier (Chapter 4).

During the 1980s, Intel chips gradually came to dominate the computer market. At the time of writing (1992), they account for over 40% of the market, and many analysts reckon that by the end of the century they will account for over 80%.

RISC microprocessors

In most CPUs, the control unit can handle a wide range of instructions. Most of these instructions are, however, infrequently used. RISC stands for *reduced instruction set computer*, and in RISC microprocessors the control unit is only able to handle the 20% most frequently-used instructions. The remaining 80%, when needed, can be obtained by combining two or more of the instructions which are available. The design of RISC chips is such that the frequently-used instructions are carried out very rapidly, far faster than on conventional chips. (A conventional chip is a 'complex instruction set computer', or CISC.)

The first microcomputer using RISC technology was the Acorn Archimedes, launched in Britain in 1987. Costing under £1,000, this machine ran several times faster than other temporary microcomputers, and was able to run applications involving intensive processing, such as graphics applications, at a speed never before seen in computers in this price range.

Today, RISC chips are available from both Intel and Motorola. Intel's main RISC chip, the i860, is compatible with its 80 × 86 chip series, and so can be incorporated into standard PCs. Its latest chip in the 80 × 86 series, the 80586 (not yet in production at the time of writing), will incorporate RISC technology. Also, new chips are available which incorporate both RISC and CISC technologies. Motorola's new 68040 processor incorporates both, the computers that use this are able to run at very high speeds.

The transputer

Short for *transistor computer*, the transputer contains, on a single chip, both the CPU and some memory, as well as communications channels to link it to other transputers. It is a RISC chip, so processing is very fast, and the fact that transputers can be linked means that they can process instructions in parallel.

The type of processing carried out in conventional computers is called *serial processing*. In this, the instructions contained in a program are carried out one after the other. This works well enough in office administration applications such as word processing and record keeping, which make relatively light demands of the CPU, but it is quite inadequate for very heavy processing tasks such as image recognition or speech recognition (see later).

To illustrate the problem, imagine how you would get on if you tried to recognize a face by breaking it down into a series of points and examining each in turn (i.e. serially). The task would take ages. What the brain does, in fact, is to examine each point simultaneously, so that you are able to instantly recognize the face. This is called *parallel processing*.

Because the transputer is a parallel processing device, any equipment that is based upon it will be able to operate more like the human brain, capable of carrying out the kind of complex recognition tasks that we take in our stride. The hope is that the next generation of IT equipment will be able to recognize and act upon speech, drawn images, handwritten instructions, and so on, as readily as we can.

Neural networks

Neural networks attempt to take computing even closer to the human brain. Even with parallel processing, computers are vastly outperformed by the brain at tasks such as image recognition. On the face of it, this is surprising, since current computers process data about a million times faster than the brain!

The reason is that the brain is able to learn from experience. In effect, it uses its experiences to build up generalized sets of rules, and then uses these to discern the essential characteristics in a mass of otherwise irrelevant data. This is what allows it to recognize instantly a face, a voice, an object, etc. What happens at the physical level in the brain is that successive experiences of a similar type build up and strengthen particular neurons. (Neurons are the filament-like tissue that carry electrical pulses of data in the brain.)

Neural networks are an attempt to mimic this learning activity of the brain. They consist of layers of simulated neurons on a silicon chip. The connections between these and the input and output nodes on the chip are strengthened or weakened according to the 'experiences' of the chip. Alternatively, neural networks can be software simulations running on conventional computers – these are much cheaper, but much slower than using specially built chips.

To use a neural network, you first have to train it by repeatedly inputting samples of information it has to recognize, 'telling' it what that information is by indicating what its outputs should be. Eventually it builds up its internal connections so that it can reliably produce the desired output from other samples of information. In this way you can, for example, train a network to recognize letters of the alphabet written in a variety of hands. You present it with a series of a's, b's, c's etc., indicating at the same time the appropriate sequence of bits that correspond to each.

Neural networks are starting to be used in a variety of applications, including checking airport baggage for explosives and weapons, listening to car engines to spot defects, and picking out trends in financial trading data.

Digital signal processors

Digital signal processors (DSPs) are used in voice recognition systems, computer video applications such as interactive compact disc, complex mathematical calculations, music synthesis, as well as in more standard bits of equipment such as disk controllers and modems. They allow the high-speed processing of digital signals from audio, video, and other sources.

DSPs are microchips optimized to carry out, at high speeds and with a high degree of accuracy, complex numerical calculations. They incorporate a number of enhancements to increase the processing speed. These may include dual arithmetic logic units, separate program and data memories, and high-speed memory access. This makes them suitable for numerically intensive processing applicatons such as those listed above.

The first high-speed DSP was produced by AT & T in 1978. Since then Motorola, Texas Instruments, and others have produced DSPs, and these chips are now incorporated into a wide range of devices.

Processing speeds

The main way in which a computer's power is judged is the speed at which it runs. This depends upon two factors:

● the speed of its internal clock, measured in millions of cycles per second (megahertz, or MHz for short)
● the average number of clock cycles it requires to execute an instruction.

For example, a PC with an 80386 chip may have a clock speed of 20 or 25 MHz and will require about 4.5 clock cyles to perform an instruction. By dividing the clock speed by the number of cycles per instruction you can see that this gives a processing speed of around 5 million instructions per second (MIPS). (Compare this with the human brain – its neurons conduct electrical pulses at the frequency of about 1 kilohertz, which is snail-like in comparison.)

The purpose of the internal clock is to ensure that all the devices in the computer act in unison. It does this by sending electrical pulses through the system. The speed at which the clock is able to run is limited not only by the speed of the CPU but also the speed of the other components. So replacing an 8086 processor in an old PC by an 80386 processor does not mean that the PC will be able to run at 20 or 25 MHz.

The original IBM PC with its 8086 chip supported a clock speed of 4.77 MHz. To execute the average instruction required about 15 clock cycles, so its processing speed was 0.3 MIPS. The latest PCs using the 80486 chip have clock speeds of 30 or 35 MHz and execute an instruction in just over 2 clock cycles, giving a processing speed of around 15 MIPS. The i860 RISC chip has a clock speed of around 40 MHz and executes about 1 instruction per clock cycle, giving a processing speed of around 40 MIPS – about 130 times as fast as the original PC!

For much office software, e.g. character-based word processing and record keeping, the internal processing speed of the computer may not be very important, because this kind of software does not make heavy demands of the processor (i.e. it involves relatively few instructions per period of time). On the other hand, graphics software, speech processing, and some engineering and mathematical applications, make heavy demands on the processor and so are best run on fast computers.

Increasingly, standard office applications such as word processing are being run within graphical environments such as 'Windows' (see Chapter 4), and fast PCs, preferably based on the 80386 processor or above, are best for this. In fact, the PC world seems to be splitting into two camps, those with slower and cheaper computers running character-based software, and those with the more expensive models running graphics-based software within the Windows environment. As I shall explain later, for certain applications a graphics environment is highly desirable; however, for many run-of-the-mill office applications there is little point in using this environment and, indeed, certain advantages in remaining in the character-based world.

Computer memory

'Memory' is an area of storage within the computer where programs and data are held ready for processing by the CPU. The significant feature of memory, compared to disk storage, is that the CPU can access it at extremely high speeds, and any delays caused by moving data in and out of memory are therefore minimized. When you 'load' a file from disk, you are in fact copying it into an area of memory. However, compared to disk, memory is expensive and limited. The typical PC has less than 4 Mbyte of memory, but 40, 80, or 120 Mbyte of hard disk capacity, and access to an indefinite number of floppy disks.

Computer memory is of two types, *RAM* and *ROM*. These are explained below.

Random access memory

Random access memory, or RAM, is a temporary store for holding programs and data loaded from disk, or typed at the keyboard, or input from some other device. The term 'random access' means that the data can be picked out of the memory in any order, and contrasts with 'sequential access', which is the kind of access you get with magnetic tape and some other storage devices, where the data has to be read in sequence, starting at the beginning and working through to the end.

Nowadays, a RAM device is normally a silicon chip, made up of thousands of tiny (transistor) switches, each of which can be either ON or OFF, and so represent a binary digit (1 or 0). Memory of this type is *volatile*, meaning that its contents are lost when the power is turned off.

In the case of mainframe computers, core store memory was normally used. The memory devices in this case are tiny magnetic rings, threaded onto a matrix of criss-crossing wires. The direction of magnetization in a ring is determined by the current flowing through the wires, one direction representing a binary 0, the other a binary 1. Because the rings remain magnetized even when the power is turned off, the data is retained. So this type of memory is called *non-volatile*.

In both types of memory, the individual devices – transistors or rings – are laid out in rectangular arrays, each one occupying a location or *address* that can be identified by its row and column numbers. These numbers are, of course, in binary digital form. Each item of data stored in memory therefore has associated with it a *memory address*.

When the CPU reads an item of data from memory, it has to do two things:

1 look up the address of the data in memory
2 read the data, i.e. the sequence of 0s and 1s, at that address.

The numbers identifying memory addresses travel in electronic form down an *address bus* inside the computer, those representing the data travel down a *data bus*.

Read only memory

Read only memory, or ROM, is a permanent store on microchip, normally used for holding programs. In this type of memory the tiny transistor switches cannot be turned ON or OFF, but are permanently encoded at the time of the chip's manufacture to produce the required program. These chips are called *read only*, because it is not possible to write new programs or data to them.

The advantage of using ROM chips instead of storing data on disk and reading it into RAM as required is:

● it is more convenient to have frequently used software immediately available inside the computer instead of on disk
● when the computer is running, all of the RAM is left free of data (though note that for the PC the 640K limit applies to ROM and RAM combined).

If the computer has a hard disk (see next chapter), the first of these is of little account, as the software can be almost as quickly loaded from the hard disk. However, ROM-based software is useful (sometimes essential) in the case of notebook computers which may lack a hard disk (or sometimes any sort of disk).

The disadvantages of ROM-based software are:

● the relatively high cost compared to disk storage
● it may by difficult to upgrade to later versions of the software.

Some ROMs can be erased and reprogrammed. These are called EPROMS (short for Erasable Programmable ROM). You can recognize one of these by the small glass window in the surface of its casing, below which is the actual microchip (see Figure 1.1). The contents of the chip can be erased by exposing it to ultraviolet light for about 20 minutes, and it can then be reprogrammed by loading a new program into it.

The memory map

I've said that memory on the PC is limited to 640K. This is not strictly true – the CPU is able to access up to 1 Mb. However, the area of memory above 640K (the top 360K) is reserved for system tasks such as controlling the output to the monitor. The 640K is the amount of memory reserved for programs and data, including the operating system itself which takes up about 40K. (The exact amount depends on the version on the operating system.)

It is in fact possible to add many Mbytes of 'expanded' memory. The CPU is not able to access this directly, but what it can do is swap a 64K chunk of this memory into a 64K 'page frame' located in the top 360K of ordinary memory, and access that. By rapidly swapping different 64K pages of expanded memory in and out of this page frame area, it can in effect scan the entire memory.

For this to work, the expanded memory has to conform to the so-called LIM (Lotus-Intel-Microsoft) standard, and any software which wishes to use this facility has to be written to this standard. It sounds complicated, but it works well enough. In fact the software I am using to write the second edition of this book, and the text itself, are residing in the expanded memory area of my computer, leaving virtually the entire 640K of ordinary memory free for other things. This means that I can run other software at the same time, should I so wish, and jump instantly between my writing work and other computing activities.

Types of computer

Computers can be classified in a variety of ways. Traditionally, they have been divided into *mainframe, mini,* and *microcomputers,* but with the increasing power of microcomputers this distinction is becoming blurred.

The largest type of computer is the *mainframe,* which takes its name from the big metal cabinet or 'frame' which was originally required to house the central processing unit. In the past, a mainframe might occupy a large room and cost millions of pounds (and be less powerful than modern PCs!). Even today it must be housed in a number of sizeable cabinets, and costs are of the order of £100 000 and upwards. A mainframe can cope with the data processing requirements of a large business, having the following advantages over smaller computers:

● it processes data at higher speeds, and so handles large jobs more quickly
● the disk drives can store much more data than is possible in a smaller system, and they can therefore handle larger files
● its operating system allows a number of people to use it simultaneously, through a technique called *multiprogramming*. They are connected to it by keyboard-and-screen units called *terminals* or *visual display units* (VDUs).

Minicomputers are cut-down mainframes, often costing between £10 000 and £20 000, and able to handle the work of smaller organizations. A mini will be smaller than a mainframe, its storage capacity will be smaller, and it will not be able to support so many users at the same time.

Microcomputers are the desktop machines that have swept the computer scene in the last decade. They include hand-held devices and home computers, as well as business machines. The latter are called *personal computers*, because they are intended for the use of a single indivdual rather than for shared use by a number of people.

Today, personal computers are often *networked*, meaning that they are connected by cable to each other and to central facilities such as large hard disks and printers. Networked PCs can, in many organizations, perform the type of task that required mainframe or minicomputers in the past. They can share large files of data, and, with the processing speeds of modern microprocessors, execute large data processing tasks at high speeds.

Personal computers are therefore taking over much of the computing work in many organizations, leaving mainframes and minis for specialist tasks requiring massive processing such as airline booking systems, banking systems, and factory control. Even these areas may eventually be taken over by the next generation of RISC-based microcomputers that are now beginning to appear.

Computer generations

Another way of classifying computers is by generation.

● The *first generation* of computers were in operation in the 1950s, and their CPUs were built with thermionic valves. As explained earlier, these computers were very large, expensive, and unreliable, and their performance was feeble by today's standards. (Today's computers are about a million times faster!) Also, they consumed a great deal of electricity and generated a lot of heat, so cooling systems had tó built in. Internal memory was by means of magnetic drums (similar in principle to today's magnetic disks), so memory access times were slow.

● The *second generation* were in operation in the early 1960s, the thermionic valves being replaced by transistors (which at that time had to be soldered together rather than incorporated into a chip). These were smaller, cheaper, and more reliable than valves, and they consumed less electricity and produced less heat. They were about a thousand times faster than first-generation computers. Internal memory was by means of core storage.

● The *third generation* came into existence in the mid-1960s, when microchips became available (consisting of many transistors and other components etched onto the surface of the chip). These were much smaller, cheaper, and faster than individual transistors soldered together. Processing times increased by a further factor of 1000 at this time. Another characteristic of the third generation was the appearance of high-level programming languages such as COBOL and FORTRAN (see Chapter 4).

● *Fourth-generation computers* are characterized by chips exhibiting very large-scale integration (VLSI) of components. VLSI chips were developed at the start of the 1970s, and are, in effect, computers on a chip. Fourth-generation computers are generally dated from the mid-1970s, and include the current generation of microcomputers. Various software innovations also characterize this generation, including systems network architecture and fourth-generation programming languages.

● The *fifth generation* is still largely on the drawing board, and is characterized by its ability to handle image recognition, speech recognition, and other artificial intelligence capabilities. Parallel processing techniques based on RISC chips (or their successors) will be a feature of these computers.

The evolution of the personal computer

Computers have been with us for less than half a century, yet they have transformed our world. The biggest change has taken place over the last 15 years, with the advent of fourth-generation computers, especially personal computers. There are now over 50 million personal computers in use worldwide. Their impact has been so profound that it's worth devoting a few pages to their evolution.

The first microcomputers appeared in the mid-1970s. They included the legendary Apple I and Apple II computers, and the Commodore PET. These computers were little more than toys by today's standards, endowed with a mere 16K of memory or less,. storage by means of cassette tape, and low-powered 8-bit processors. Nevertheless, they were cheap (by the standards of the day), easy to use, and you could use them to write letters and, if you were an enthusiast, to program.

What brought these computers to the attention of the business community was the appearance of a program called Visicalc. This was the world's first spreadsheet, and it was written for the Apple. It turned out to be just the kind of thing that managers and decision makers needed (see Chapter 8), and so large numbers of them bought the Apple just to run Visicalc.

The dominant computer company, IBM, manufactured only large computers at this time, and was reluctant to move into micros. One reason for this reluctance was the fact that micros on managers' desks threatened the power and the jobs of the people who actually purchased IBM's products, namely data processing personnel. Another was the destabilizing effect that such micros would have on IBM's large and profitable mainframe market.

However, by the start of the 1980s the highly successful Apple computer was making significant inroads into the business computing market, and IBM had to respond. In August 1981 it launched its first microcomputer, the original PC.

The IBM PC

Technologically, the PC was no great advance on the older Apple and PET microcomputers. There were problems with the keyboard, the screen resolution was not all that good, it had only 64K of memory, and the operating system (DOS) was simply a rehash of the older CP/M operating system. The reason for the PC's remarkable success was the badge on the front that said 'IBM'.

At that time, IBM dominated the computer market to a much greater extent than it does today. It offered its customers a coherent range of products, with a natural upgrade route from less powerful to more powerful and from older to newer. It offered them maintenance and other support, and it offered them the security of dealing with a supplier who, without doubt, was not going to collapse and disappear. Apple Computing, however good its product, could offer none of these benefits – although, in retrospect, it has not disappeared and in the second half of the 1980s and early 1990s enjoyed a marked increase in popularity and profitability.

IBM's entry into the microcomputer market provided just the push that commerce and industry needed to embrace this most important component of the information technology revolution. Companies were prepared to buy the PC because the IBM badge gave it credibility. Software houses were prepared to write packages for it, because there was a large and growing market. More people were prepared to buy the PC because of this growing range of software, and this encouraged yet more software houses to enter the fray. An exponential growth set in, with ever more customers buying and ever more and better software being sold, to the benefit of all. The PC had set the industry standard for producers and users, and the microcomputer had come of age.

But this benign circle of users and software producers was not the only reason for the wholesale adoption of the PC. Another factor helped to fuel the boom, one which IBM had built into its computer without realizing where it would lead.

The clones and the add-ons

Whatever the defects of IBM's personal computer, it had two uniquely redeeming features that have greatly helped the IT revolution:

- it was an *open architecture* machine, meaning that it was designed to be expandable by adding on additional circuitry
- its design can easily be copied.

The large and growing PC market encouraged other manufacturers to exploit these features, to the advantage of everyone (except possibly IBM).

- There are many companies offering a variety of *expansion cards,* i.e. circuit boards containing chips which can be fixed in the expansion slots inside the PC's casing. These cards offer a range of facilities and enhancements, including improved screen displays, speech recognition, greater processing power, and so on.
- There are now many companies making and assembling personal computers which are virtually identical to the IBM PC and its successors. These are called *PC-compatibles,* or *clones.* They are able to run the same software as the real thing, but are normally cheaper and often offer superior performance.

What is so extraordinary is that although these computers comprise by far the largest segment of the market, IBM itself no longer manufactures them!

The IBM AT

As was explained earlier, the IBM PC was based on the Intel 8086 chip. This was looking distinctly long in the tooth by the mid-1980s, and it made the PC look weak beside some of the newer micros that were appearing, especially the Apple Macintosh (see below).

In August 1984 IBM launched the PC-AT. ('AT' stood for 'advanced technology' – some would claim that this was more of a marketing ploy than a statement of truth!) This was designed to be compatible with the PC (i.e. run the same software) but to overcome some of the earlier machine's defects. One obvious external difference was the improved keyboard. Internally it had a more advanced CPU, based on the Intel 80286 chip. This enabled it to:

- run a lot faster
- access memory above the 640K limit (in theory)
- run several programs simultaneously (called *multi-tasking*)
- allow simultaneous use of the CPU and hard disk by several users (called *multi-using*).

In practice, however, the full potential of this machine has never been exploited, so that it has been used simply as a fast PC. The reason is that the enhancements to the operating system necessary

41

for it to access more memory and to multi-task have yet to materialize (though Windows version 3 has finally arrived on the scene which does enable this).

The Apple Macintosh

The original Apple microcomputer brought to birth personal computing in business. It was conquered by the IBM PC, but Apple fought back with the Macintosh, which appeared shortly before the IBM AT. The Mac was far ahead of its day in terms of both hardware and software. It was based upon a much more powerful processor, the 68000 chip, and it introduced a way of working with computers which is only now becoming standard on the IBM PC family.

This way of working was based upon Rank Xerox's original research work in the 1970s, and involved the use of the mouse to point to different parts of the screen and to pick options, the use of a graphical rather than character-based display, and the use of icons (pictorial representations of computing entities such as files). Also, some excellent applications packages appeared for the Mac, which made full use of its graphical environment. A particular software innovation was desktop publishing, made possible by the Mac environment and the appearance, in the mid-1980s, of the desktop laser printer (see Chapter 3).

By 1987/88 the Mac was so far ahead in terms of graphics and publishing applications of anything that was available in the IBM PC world that it even seemed possible that it might topple IBM and its followers from their pre-eminent position. In the event, this has never happened. The reasons include:

● corporate inertia against moving from the accepted standard
● high prices of the Mac, and Apple's policy of keeping out competing manufacturers who would bring prices down
● the knowledge that the PC world was moving towards, and catching up with, the Mac world.

Today, the IBM PC world has effectively caught up with the Mac in terms of the power of the hardware and the user interface. In retrospect, we can see that the value of the Mac was to popularize Xerox's revolutionary computer working environment, so that it is now the standard across almost the entire range of serious personal computing. As at the start of the 1980s, at the start of the 1990s Apple has proved to be the pace setter but not the victor.

The IBM PS/2

In 1987 IBM ceased production of PCs and ATs, and brought out in their place its new PS/2 range (short for Personal System/2). These are based on the same Intel chips as the PC and AT, and able to run standard PC software. However, they incorporated the superior *MicroChannel Architecture* (see below), and the superior VGA screen display (see page 62). They also offered a Mac-like computing environment called 'Presentation Manager'. A further advantage for users with IBM mainframe is their ability to easily connect with these and so act as terminals.

IBM hoped that large numbers of corporate users would abandon the old PC/AT standard and flock to its new machine. In fact, this has not happened. PC/AT machines seem to go from strength to strength. They continue to outsell all others, they are steadily becoming more and more powerful, and they have adopted the VGA screen display standard. Besides this, the new Windows version 3 environment for the PC is virtually identical to Presentation Manager, and a huge amount of applications software is currently being written for it – far more than is being produced for Presentation Manager.

Computer buses

The 'bus' in a computer is the wiring along which all the bits that make up each item of the information travel in parallel. An important feature of the IBM PC's bus is its expansion capability – it provides a series of slots into which expansion cards can be added. The original PC bus allowed only 8 bits to travel in parallel; when it introduced the AT in 1984, IBM doubled the number of wires in the bus so that it could handle 16 bits, and it also doubled its speed to 8 MHz. The AT bus has proved very successful, there are a large number of expansion cards available for it, and it is still the standard in the PC world. It is now referred to as the *Industry Standard Architecture* (ISA) bus.

One of the main features of the IBM PS/2 range of computers which were introduced in 1987 was the radically new *MicroChannel*

Architecture (MCA) bus. This offered a number of advantages over the AT bus:

- it doubled the number of wires to handle 32 bits
- it could run much faster
- it offered improved multi-tasking capabilities
- it allowed expansion cards to use the bus without imposing additional work on the CPU
- it allowed PS/2 computers to be directly linked to IBM mainframe and minicomputers and so act as terminals.

However, it was not compatible with the AT bus, which meant that PS/2 computers lost an essential element of PC compatibility, for they could not use any existing expansion cards.

To compete with the superior technology of MCA, other PC manufacturers led by Compaq announced (in 1988) that a new *Extended Industry Standard Architecture* (EISA) bus would be developed. Like MCA, this would be a 32-bit bus and would run at a high speed, but it would be compatible with the ISA bus and so take existing expansion cards. The EISA bus is now available, and is provided as standard on many 80486 machines.

Being 32-bit, MCA and EISA buses are significantly more expensive than the 16-bit ISA bus. At present they have little to offer most users, as few expansion cards are able to take advantage of the high speeds that they allow.

Assignment 2

As camp leader, there is a range of applications that you have for a computer. There are certainly administrative tasks that you wish to perform, but there may also be other needs like artwork, animation, and music, depending on the interests of your club.

a Write a report identifying the type of microcomputer that is most suitable – e.g. 80x86-based, or 680x0-based – giving reasons for your choice.

b Choose one model of computer from the range you have chosen, and write a brief description of it, illustrating your answer with appropriate sales brochures for that computer.

Recap

- A computer consists of *hardware*, which enables it to carry out the input–store–process–output sequence automatically, and *software*, which tells it how to carry out the task in hand. Different software programs enable the computer to be used for different tasks.

- A *microprocessor* is a complex electrical circuit etched on a sliver of silicon. It contains thousands of *transistors*, which act as electrically operated switches.

- These transistors are organized into *logic gates*, which are able to perform the logical operations AND, OR, and NOT, and logic gates are organized into more complex circuits such as *half-adders*, which perform arithmetical calculations. This is why microprocessors can be used in IT devices such as calculators and computers.

- A transistor may be used to form a *bistable* device, which means it is in only one of two states. One of these states may be used to represent the digit 0, the other the digit 1. So in a microprocessor, all information has to be handled as numerical data in the form of 0s and 1s. These are called *binary numbers*, and microprocessors operate using binary arithmetic.

- The microprocessor inside the computer which performs the computations is called the *central processing unit*. There are a number of designs of microprocessor CPU, including the Z80, the 6502, the 80386, and the 68000. The first two of these are 8-bit chips, meaning that they handle data only 8 bits at a time. This means that they are relatively slow, and can access only 64 Kbytes of memory. The second two are 32-bit chips, meaning that they handle data 32 bits at a time. They are very fast, and are capable of accessing up to 16 Mbytes of memory.

- A significant development in microprocessor technology is the *transputer*. This device is designed for *parallel processing*, so that it will be able to carry out efficiently tasks such as image recognition and speech recognition.

- *Neural networks* attempt to mimic the learning activity of the brain. They consist of layers of simulated neurons on a silicon chip. The connections between these are strengthened or weakened by the 'experiences' of the chip, mimicking the way in which connections between neurons are built up in the brain.

- *Digital signal processors* are another type of chip, optimized to carry out complex numerical calculations. They are used in voice recognition systems, interactive compact disc, and other applications requiring high-speed processing of digital signals.

● Computers have internal clocks which ensure that all parts of the system work in unison. The clock speed is limited by the speeds of the various components, in particular the CPU. Modern software environments such as Windows require computers with high clock speeds to run effectively. Clock speeds are measured in MHz, and modern PCs typically run at around 25 MHz.

● Computer memory devices include semiconductor *RAM* for holding programs and data currently in use, or, in the case of large computers, *core store*. Core store is made up of tiny magnetic rings and, unlike semiconductor RAM, is *non-volatile*, i.e. it retains its contents when power is turned off. ROM chips are available, on which programs are etched during the manufacturing process. These are a convenient way of storing certain programs on some systems.

● Computers can be classified as *mainframe*, *mini*, and *microcomputers*, though the distinction between these types is becoming blurred. They can also be classified by *generation*: successive generations reflect the increasing power and integration of the CPU components, and the increasing sophistication of the system software.

● During the 1980s and 1990s the phenomenal growth of personal computing has transformed information technology. The main types are the PC, originally brought out by IBM and based on the Intel 80×86 family of chips, and the Apple Macintosh, based on the Motorola 680×0 chip family.

● The main wiring inside the computer along which data travels in parallel is called the *bus*. Several bus designs are in use, including ISA (used on the PC/AT) and MCA (used on the PS/2).

Answers to questions

1 An ordinary pocket calculator has a data capture device (the keypad), a storage and processing device (a microprocessor), and a communicating device (a one-line display), all linked by wires so that they can carry out arithmetic operations on data automatically. It also has built into it a program of instructions telling these devices how to perform these operations. It differs from a computer in that it cannot be given other programs of instructions to carry out different tasks.

2 E is represented by the number 01000101, and so the sequence of switches is OFF-ON-OFF-OFF-OFF-ON-OFF-ON.

3 The table is correct.

Line 2 means: if *Ann is going* is false, and if *Barbara is going* is true, then *Ann and Barbara are (both) going* is false.

Line 3 means: if *Ann is going* is true, and if *Barbara is going* is false, then *Ann and Barbara are (both) going* is false.

Line 4 means: if *Ann is going* is true, and if *Barbara is going* is true, then *Ann and Barbara are (both) going* is true.

4 The table is correct.

Line 1 means: if *Ann is going* is false, and if *Barbara is going* is false, then *Either Ann or Barbara are going* is false.

Line 2 means: if *Ann is going* is false, and if *Barbara is going* is true, then *Either Ann or Barbara is going* is true.

Line 3 means: if *Ann is going* is true, and if *Barbara is going* is false, then *Ann or Barbara is going* is true.

Line 4 means: if *Ann is going* is true, and if *Barbara is going* is true, then *Ann or Barbara (or both) are going* is true.

5 The last two lines of the truth table are:

1 0 1 1 1
1 1 1 0 0

3: Computer peripherals and applications

Objectives

After reading this chapter, you should be able to:
- outline the operations a computer performs when it executes commands typed at the keyboard or stored in a program
- describe the main peripherals of a computer system, including the keyboard, mouse, disk-drive, monitor, and printer, and explain the tasks they perform
- indicate the main applications of computers, and describe the main benefits that arise from their use in those applications.

Scenario

As the youth club leader in charge of the summer camp, you have many administrative tasks to perform. You may also have artwork to produce. How will a computer help you with these tasks?

Activity

If you have not already done so, it is essential that you spend some time at a computer before getting too far into this chapter. Most computers are supplied with introductory booklets and programs, and if you are new to computers, it's a good idea to begin by working through these. If you have access to a BBC micro, try the 'Welcome' disk that is supplied with it.

Using a computer

A *peripheral* is a device which is outside the central processing unit of a computer but controlled by it. There are four main types of peripheral, namely input devices such as keyboards, storage devices such as magnetic disks, output devices such as monitors and printers, and communication devices such as modems.

The previous chapter dealt with computers in general and covered the work of the CPU. This chapter covers the peripheral devices that might be connected to it. Modems and other telecommunications devices are covered in Chapter 6.

By way of introduction, let's look at how a computer system operates. On many home computers, you can type

PRINT 2★4

and the computer responds by displaying the answer 8 on the monitor. In this example, you are typing in two *commands*, namely the command to multiply (★) and the command to display the result on the output device (PRINT), and two items of data, i.e. the number 2 and the number 4.

The sequence of operations that takes place in the computer to perform this task is as follows:

● Each of the characters typed at the keyboard is converted to binary digital form, becoming a sequence of 0s and 1s. These digits are converted to electrical pulses which travel in parallel down the wire from the keyboard to the CPU.

● The CPU is able to distinguish between the commands (namely PRINT and ★) and the data (2 and 4). The commands are handled by the control unit in the CPU, whereas the data is routed to the arithmetic logic unit, where it is stored in a special area of memory.

● Next, the control unit obeys the ★ command by instructing the ALU to carry out the calculation.

● The control unit then obeys the PRINT command by routing the result of the calculation to the monitor, where it is displayed.

A more complex task may involve many hundreds or thousands of commands, and large amounts of data. An example might be the word processing task that my computer is currently carrying out, involving the input and processing of these words that I'm writing. In this case the commands will be strung together in a *program* (i.e. the word processing program I am using), which is stored on disk, and the words will also be stored on disk in a *data file* (i.e. the file that I am creating as I type this chapter).

In outline, the computer performs the following operations to execute this task:

● *loads* the program, i.e. makes a copy of it in RAM
● *loads* the data file, i.e. makes a copy of it in RAM
● *updates* the file (in RAM) by obeying the command sequences in the word processing program telling it how to add the additional words that I type and how to incorporate any amendments I make to existing material
● *saves* the file, i.e. makes a copy of the updated file onto disk
● *prints* the updated file, if I ask for this, by sending its contents down the wire to the printer connected to my computer.

All these operations involve commands and data in binary form. For example, to load the program from disk into RAM, the disk-drive generates a stream of electrical pulses corresponding to the magnetized/demagnetized spots on the part of the disk's surface on which the program is stored, and this stream produces a corresponding pattern of ON/OFF switches in RAM.

In this chapter we'll look at some of the input, storage, processing and output devices that the computer uses to carry out its operations. I should emphasize that this is not an exhaustive survey of all the devices available, though I have tried to cover the main ones.

Question

1 As camp leader you decide to draw the route map to the camp using a computer drawing package. Using the above list as a guide, outline the operations the computer will perform.

Input devices

A variety of input devices exist, able to convert information in any form (data, text, voice, or image) into the binary pulses recognized by computers. Some of these devices are described below.

The keyboard

The keyboard is still the primary device for inputting information to a computer, though it may ultimately be superseded by voice input devices. It operates by converting key presses to electronic signals in binary digital form.

The typical computer keyboard has the standard 'QWERTY' character keys inherited from the typewriter, together with a number of special keys described below. Alternative keyboard layouts have been designed, incorporating a more logical and natural arrangement of character keys, but these have never caught on.

The special keys vary somewhat according to the make of computer, but they usually include the following:

- *Function keys*, up to 12 in number, positioned either above or to the left of the character keys. These can be programmed by the user or by the software being run, so that a single key depression sends a command or string of commands to the computer.
- *The CTRL and ALT keys* (short for Control and Alternate), which are always used in conjunction with other keys to issue commands to the computer. For example, in the WordStar word processing software, CTRL and G, pressed at the same time, delete the character at the cursor position on the screen, CTRL and T delete the word at this position, and CTRL and Y delete the line.
- *The backspace key*, which deletes the character to the immediate left of the cursor on the screen.
- *The four 'arrow' keys*, which move the cursor one character position in the direction of the arrow (up, down, left, or right).
- *The PgUp and PgDn keys*, which are normally programmed by your word processing or other software to move the cursor one 'page' (i.e. screen) up or down.
- *The Home key*, which may be programmed to move the cursor to the left of the screen, or the beginning of the document.
- *The End key*, which may be programmed to move the cursor to the right of the screen, or the end of the document.
- *The Esc key*, which is often programmed to enable you to escape from your currently selected option or task.

The mouse

The *mouse* is a hand-held device with a rubber or metal ball protruding from its base (see Figure 3.1). As you push the mouse over the surface of the desk, the movements of the ball are detected by the internal mechanism and converted to electrical signals.

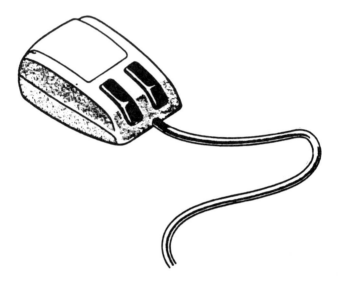

Figure 3.1 The Microsoft mouse

These are fed to the computer via a cable and converted by the associated software to corresponding movements of the cursor across the screen. At the front of the mouse's casing are two or three buttons (or a single button in the case of the Macintosh mouse). You press these to perform tasks such as picking options displayed on the screen.

Similar to the mouse is the trackerball, used on some computers. In this, the casing remains stationary while the ball, which is at the top, is rolled with the fingers.

The mouse has proved very popular, and is now utilized by a great deal of software. In particular, it is much easier to use than the keyboard for the following operations:

- *picking*, i.e. selecting options from a list displayed on the screen
- *pointing*, i.e. moving rapidly from one point to another in a word-processed document, file of records, or table of data
- *drawing*, i.e. constructing lines and other shapes on the screen.

On some computer systems, such as the Apple Macintosh, the Atari ST, the IBM PS/2, and PCs running Windows, the mouse is an essential part of the hardware, as the way in which you use the software on those systems is to a large extent, based upon it. With other systems, such as PCs which do not use the Windows environment, the mouse is not essential, though some software running on those systems cannot easily be used without it.

Character-recognition devices

One type of character-recognition device enables the user to input text and numerical data by handwriting it in capital letters on the presure-sensitive surface using a special pen. An invisible grid of fine wires below the surface detects the shape of the letters. converting them to electrical signals which the computer interprets using special software. Although this device is a genuine replacement for the keyboard, it has never really caught on, being overtaken by other developments, in particular the advances being made in speech-recognition devices described later.

Much more useful are the optical character readers (OCRs) which scan text which has been typed or printed on paper, converting the characters to the binary code that the computer understands. These provide a way of passing information between machines which cannot communicate electronically. For example, they enable output from a typewriter to be passed to a word processor for editing and final printing, a technique that has been used in some typing pools. They also enable a business to convert its input documents to electronic form without the need to key them in.

Some modern image scanners, described later in this chapter, can also function as OCRs when used with special OCR software. These can recognize a reasonable range of typefaces, so enabling printed and typed text to be input to a computer. However, smeared characters and unusual typefaces may be beyond them. In place of a character that they can't recognize, they will substitute a special symbol. These symbols can be automatically picked out and replaced later on with the aid of spell-checking software.

The microphone

It is quite easy to convert the spoken word to a digital signal for computer input. The microphone coverts audio signals to electrical waves, and these can be coverted by electronic circuitry in the computer to digital form. What is difficult is the recognition, by the computer, of the signal, so that it can handle it in the same way as if it had been typed. Highly sophisticated speech-recognition software is required, able to match the sound uttered by the user with a vocabulary of sound signals stored in the computer, and to display the words on the screen as though they had been entered at the keyboard.

The development of viable speech-recognition systems for the English language have been a major goal of many researchers for a number of years. Recently, commercial systems have started to emerge. One major problem is the many inconsistencies between the written and spoken word in English. Japanese, in contrast, is phonetically very precise, and so speech-recognition systems for that language were relatively easy to develop and have been used for some time. English-language systems face the task of having to infer, from the context, what the words are likely to be.

A second problem is the fact that there can be wide variations between the speech patterns of one individual and another. To cope with this, the system has to be 'trained' to recognize the user's particular speech. Most systems require him or her to read a passage containing all the words stored in the computer's vocabulary on disk, so that it is able to match what's spoken with what's stored. In this way it constructs speech 'templates' for the user, which it stores for use in all subsequent dictation sessions.

Speech-recognition systems in the past have suffered from either having too limited a vocabulary to be of much use, or else, in the case of large vocabulary systems, taking far too long to match what was spoken with what was stored in the computer. Recent increases in computer power have greatly speeded things up, and voice systems on personal computers have now appeared. The system from Apricot is called 'Dictate', and it has a vocabulary of 30 000 words. IBM has also developed a system for PCs. At the heart of the IBM system is a digital signal processor (DSP) which uses parallel processing techniques and is able to perform 10 million instructions per second.

The system works by recognizing the 200 or more phonetic elements of words, rather than by attempting to recognize a vast vocabulary of whole words. This means that the computer has to produce only a relatively small number of speech templates, and so the initial training session can be quite brief. To match the spoken word with what's stored in its vocabulary, the computer uses a statistical approach based on an analysis by the IBM researchers of some 25 million words of office correspondence. This approach enables it to predict what words are likely to appear together, and so to select likely candidates from its vocabulary.

When the first word is spoken, the computer makes a tentative assessment but does not display the candidate word on the screen. When the next word is spoken, the initial candidate is reassessed and either accepted or rejected in favour of another, and the result displayed. The process continues through the dictation session.

Video cameras and scanners

Video cameras are versatile devices, being able to capture images of any type, including solid objects. Scanners are limited to images on paper, but they are able to scan each spot on the paper with much greater accuracy than cameras, and so are more widely used for this type of input. Scanners provide a low-cost way of inputting material that's been typed or printed on paper into a computer system. (I say 'low cost' because rekeying an A4 page costs between £4 and £5.) More was said on this earlier in this chapter on page 53.

Most scanners incorporate a special sort of camera made up of *charged-coupled devices* (CCDs). Each CCD receives light from the image, and, provided the light is strong enough, will generate an electrical charge. This means that light areas or 'dots' of the image are represented by charged cells, and dark areas by uncharged cells. As the paper containing the image moves past the camera during the scanning process, these charges create electrical impulses which are fed into the computer, where they are interpreted by the scanning software as parts of the image.

The resolution of the typical scanner is 300 dots per inch, which means that it splits each square inch of the image up into a matrix of 300 × 300 tiny areas. This is better than the resolution of most computer screens, and the same as the resolution of most laser printers (see later in this chapter). Scanners typically cost between £1000 and £2000.

The technology behind this is well-understood and quite straightforward. Nowadays, scanners are widely used to get drawings, diagrams, and photographs into computer systems for incorporation into documents and books which are made up electronically prior to printing. Much more difficult is the recognition of the image by the computer, so that it is able to act upon what it 'sees'. Just as the speech-recognition system described in the previous section worked by breaking down the spoken word into its phonetic elements, so image-recognition systems work by breaking down the image into component parts, identifying each, and analysing their position relative to each other.

Image-recognition systems have been used for some years in industrial robots, but these devices have a limited 'vocabulary' of components, and the recognition process is highly complex and so relatively slow. It seems likely that the application of the transputer and parallel processing techniques will revolutionize image processing and image recognition in the future. This may lead not only to a new generation of industrial robots but also to new computer systems and applications which are able to perform tasks such as converting hand-drawn sketches into neat designs, and recognizing faces in a crowd.

Other input devices

Other input devices include:

- *Kimball tags*, used for stock control in some clothing stores. Attached to each article of clothing is one of these tags, recording data on the article as a pattern of punched holes. When the article is sold, the tag is removed and the data scanned into the store's computer.
- *Bar codes*, used for stock control in food stores. Here, the data is stored as a pattern of thin and thick lines printed on the product's packaging; the thin lines represent binary 0s, the thick

lines 1s. At the checkout a light pen or similar device shines light across the pattern, the reflected light being translated into electrical pulses for computer input.

● *Magnetic ink character readers* (MICRs), used in banking. Cheques are identified by numbers printed with special magnetic ink, which can be read by an MICR and converted in binary digital form for computer input.

Question

2 How might the above developments in voice and image input assist you, as camp leader, in the task of producing directions to get to the camp site?

Storage devices

Because computer memory can hold only a limited amount of data and programs, and because, in the case of semiconductor RAM, it loses that data when the power is turned off, some form of long-term mass storage is essential. At present, magnetic disk is the main mass storage medium, though other types of mass storage are also used, in particular the optical disc described later.

Like the ordinary audio disc, a magnetic disk stores information on circular tracks marked out on its surface. As the disk rotates, an arm moves a read/write head to the required track, and 'reads' (i.e. retrieves) data from or 'writes' (i.e. stores) data to the spots on the track as they pass below it. The data is stored in digital form, a magnetized spot on the rotating surface representing a 1, a demagnetized spot a zero. As with an audio–cassette, information can be erased and re-recorded any number of times.

Magnetic tape can also be used in certain computer applications, but it is less versatile than disk, since it is not possible to move instantly to a particular spot on the tape to read or write data at that spot. Reading from the tape is rather like reading a novel: you must start at the beginning and read each word in sequence until you reach the end. This is called *sequential access*.

Reading from a disk is more like reading from a reference book: you look up the location of the section you require in an index and turn straight to the appropriate page. This is called *random access.* Each program or file of data on the disk must be assigned a name, and a directory of these names is stored at the beginning of the disk. The location of the file on the disk's surface is also stored in the directory, and when the computer receives a command to load a file into RAM it is able to read this location from the directory and move the read/write head directly to the required track on the disk's surface.

Floppy disks

There are two types of magnetic disk: *hard* disks (also called Winchester disks), and the smaller *floppy* disks (also called diskettes). Figure 3.2 shows the standard 5.25-inch diameter floppy disk, and as you can see it is enclosed in a protective flexible casing with an opening cut out to give the read/write head access to the magnetic surface. This type of disk is extremely light, and the disk-drive is able to bring it up to the required speed of rotation almost instantly. The disk-drive's motor only needs to be switched on by the computer when files are actually being accessed; the rest of the time the disk remains stationary in the drive.

A disk must be *formatted,* i.e. magnetically configured to run on a particular computer system, before it can be used. This process marks out sectors on the surface within which the data is stored. In the case of PCs of the IBM-compatible variety, each track on the disk is divided into nine sectors, and each sector is able to store 512 bytes of data. There are 40 tracks on each side of a standard (low-density) floppy disk, giving $40 \times 512 = 184\,320$ bytes for one side of the disk, i.e. 180 K.

In the past, cheaper disk-drives had only one read/write head, and so were able to access only one side of the disk. Modern drives are able to access both sides of the disk, so 360 K can be stored on a standard 5.25-inch floppy formatted for PCs. High-density drives on PCs allow you to store 1.2 Mbytes on two sides of a disk, though the more expensive high-density disk must be used in this case.

The smaller 3.5-inch disks are now becoming standard on personal computers (they have been used for many years on pace-setting computers such as the Apple Macintosh and the Atari ST). These disks are enclosed in a rigid plastic casing, and for added

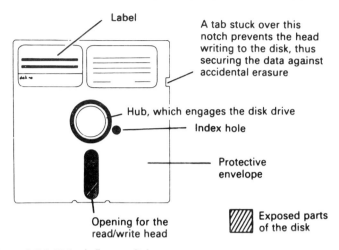

Label

A tab stuck over this notch prevents the head writing to the disk, thus securing the data against accidental erasure

Hub, which engages the disk drive

Index hole

Protective envelope

Opening for the read/write head

Exposed parts of the disk

Figure 3.2 5.25-inch floppy disk

protection the read/write opening in the case is enclosed by a metal slider when the disk is removed from the drive. Despite their smaller size, these disks can store much more data than their larger 5.25-inch brethren, namely 720 K in the case of double-sided standard density (i.e. low density) disks, and 1.44 Mbytes for high-density disks. 3.5-inch disks with capacities of 5 Mbytes or more are becoming available, and no doubt these will become the standard in the future.

Hard disks

Hard disks are so-called because, unlike floppies, they are of a sturdy, rigid construction. They are also much heavier than a floppy, and a hard disk-drive can take several seconds to get up to speed. Hard disks are therefore kept constantly spinning (while the computer is turned on), even when data is not being accessed.

The speed of rotation is very high 3600 rev/min compared to 360 rev/min for floppy disks. At this speed, the movement of the air molecules adjacent to the disk's surface lifts the read/write head sufficiently to prevent it touching the surface. It can still access the data, but it does not cause any wear on the disk. The disk and the read/write head are enclosed in an airtight casing to prevent dust particles adhering to the disk's surface and interfering with the read/write process.

Hard disks have two advantages over floppies:

● they can store much more data – typical hard disks for microcomputers have capacities of 40, 80, or 120 Mbytes
● they can access data 10 times faster than is possible with floppy disks.

Most personal computers nowadays have hard disks inside their casing. This saves fiddling with floppy disks whenever you want to load a program or load or save a file of data or text, and it greatly speeds up the loading of programs and data. Besides this, very large files, which may be too big to be held on a single floppy, will fit without difficulty onto the hard disk.

Question

3 As a youth club leader and camp organizer, do you think your computer system should include a hard disk? Jot down reasons for your answer.

Optical (compact) discs

Compact discs are the same size as standard 5.25-inch magnetic disks, but use laser-light technology to store data. Because a laser light beam can be focused with a high degree of precision, the tracks on these discs can be much closer together than is the case with magnetic disks. As a result, they have very high capacities, measured in hundreds of Mbytes (typically, 600 Mbytes). The same technology used for recording and playing music CDs is used in computer compact discs. Another advantage is the fact that data is more secure on compact discs, as it can't be corrupted by magnetic fields.

Data is encoded on an optical disc by burning tiny pits in its surface with laser light. A pit represents a binary 1, the absence of a pit represents 0. Laser light is also used to read data from the disc, the pits and non-pits setting up different light-inference patterns that can be detected by the reading head. Retrieval times are faster than floppy drives, though not as fast as hard disk systems.

Several types of compact disc systems are available for computers. These are:

- *CD-ROM.* Like music CDs, these are 'pressed' by manufacturers with whatever data they wish to supply. Large databases of information can be supplied in this way, as can software.
- *CD-WO.* This is the *WORM* drive ('Write Once, Read Many Times'), which the user can write to, but can't erase. WORM drives are an excellent medium for archiving data.
- *CD-I.* This is interactive CD, under development by Phillips for multimedia applications. This is described on page 125.
- *Erasable optical discs.* These use magneto-optical (MO) technology, and like ordinary magnetic disks allow you to record and erase data as often as you like. Unlike ordinary optical discs, the active layer of these discs is magnetized. To write a binary 1 to a spot on this layer, a pulse of laser light is focused on it, heating it up to several hundred degrees. At this temperature its magnetic polarity can be altered by a magnet which is activated on the opposite side of the disc. (The remaining cold spots will be unaffected by this magnet.) Erasable optical drives are currently very expensive, but prices will no doubt fall in the future.

Output devices: monitors

The main output devices are monitors and printers. We'll deal with monitors in this section, and printers in the next.

The resolution (or clarity) of the picture that monitors achieve is determined by the number of *pixels*, or 'picture elements', on the screen. High-resolution monitors have resolutions of 2000 by 2000 pixels, though few present-day computers are able to provide images which take advantage of this degree of clarity. The old-fashioned IBM PC, for example, with a Colour Graphics Adaptor (CGA), can only output images with a resolution of 640 pixels horizontally by 200 vertically. This was adequate for character-based displays, but for graphics it was hopelessly inferior to the displays of more advanced machines such as the Apple Macintosh.

In the mid-1980s IBM introduced the Enhanced Graphics Adaptor (EGA), which offered a higher resolution. This gave a much better clarity, though it was still not as good as the Mac.

Then, in 1987, IBM brought out the Video Graphics Array (VGA) on its PS/2 range of microcomputers, with a resolution of 640 by 480. This was quickly taken up by the PC-compatible world, and became the standard. In 1990 IBM brought out its Extended Graphics Array (XGA), with a resolution of 1024 by 768 pixels and support for 65 000 colours; 'Super VGA' with the same resolution also became available from competing manufacturers, and this is becoming the standard.

Cathode ray tubes

Most computer monitors are based on cathode ray tubes (CRTs), similar to those used in TV sets. They consist of one or more 'guns' which fire streams of electrons at a special chemical which backs the surface of the monitor. These electron streams repeatedly scan the screen from top to bottom, dot by dot and line by line, each scan taking only a fraction of a second. In colour screens, there are three guns, one for each of the colours red, green, and blue. These cause each dot on the screen to generate red, green, or blue light, the combination of these three giving the full colour spectrum. CRTs give a bright picture, with good colours, but they are bulky and consume a relatively large amount of power.

Monochrome models display text and graphics as either green on a black background, orange on a black background, or white on a black background. (The foreground and background colours can be reversed by software.) Monochrome monitors are quite cheap, and they give a sharp picture. They are well suited for office applications, such as word processing, which do not require colour.

The more expensive colour or *RGB* monitors give colour displays, but the picture sharpness on the cheaper models will not be as good as that achieved by monochrome monitors. RGB stands for Red-Green-Blue, and the CRTs in these monitors contain the three electron guns described above, each directly controlled by the computer.

Flat screens

Portable computers require screens which are light, occupy little space, and, in the case of battery-operated models, don't consume much power. The various types of flat screen that are on the market meet this need. Unlike CRTs, though, the brightness of the image is generally limited, and, at the time of writing, very few flat screen monitors give colour displays.

Liquid crystal display (LCD) monitors are used on battery-operated portable computers, as these consume very little power. (This is the type of display used on digital watches.) However, compared to CRTs the displays tend to lack contrast and in some light conditions are not very legible, though the newer 'supertwist' LCD displays are quite good.

In an LCD, the image is formed by so-called liquid crystals. These are long rod-like molecules which, though solid, can flow like a liquid. Each pixel on the screen consists of a microscopic electrode positioned below several of these molecules. As the output from the computer scans the screen a row at a time, it activates each of these pixels in turn, switching it on or off. When a pixel is 'on', the crystals twist in such a way that they block out the light. When it is 'off', they let the light through. In early LCDs, the crystals were not very 'liquid', i.e. they did not respond very rapidly to the signal, but modern types of liquid crystal are much faster.

Colour LCDs require very fast liquid crystals. In what's called *passive matrix* displays there are three screens, coloured red, green, and blue, which are placed on top of each other. Below the three screens are the thousands of pixel electrodes which generate light. The pixels in each screen act as filters for this light. If a pixel is to be red, for example, the green and blue filters above it are turned on, blocking out those colours, but the red filter is off, allowing the red light through. By turning the filters on and off in other combinations, other colours can be obtained.

Passive matrix displays are not very bright, however, since to display red, for example, light from only one out of the three crystals is allowed through the filters. They also consume too much power to be viable for battery-powered computers, and the screen refresh rate is rather slow. So *active matrix* displays are being developed, which use thin film transistor (TFT) screens. In these, there is a single screen, each pixel of which has three sub-pixels coloured red, green, and blue. These sub-pixels are separately activated to produce the colour output. Active matrix screens are, at present, difficult to manufacture and very expensive, so they are available on only a few top-of-the-range portables.

Two other types of flat screen are sometimes used for computer monitors, namely the *gas plasma* display and the *electroluminescent* display. These are both light-emitting displays, and give a very clear, legible output, but they consume almost as much power as a conventional monitor. They are therefore suitable for portable computers which are designed to run off the mains, but not for battery-powered models. These displays are monochrome-only – typically orange on a black or brown background, as this is reckoned to be both highly legible and restful on the eyes.

Question

4 As youth club leader and camp organizer, what type of monitor do you think should be purchased for your computer system? Jot down reasons for your answer.

Output devices: printers

Computer printers are used to produce *hard-copy* of computer output, normally data or text, but also, in the case of certain printers, graphics (i.e. image, such as drawings or charts). Printers vary in their capabilities so far as text enhancements (such as underlining or emboldening) are concerned, and also in their ability to print graphics.

Most printers are designed to receive data 'in parallel' from the computer, 8 bits at a time. These have to be connected to the parallel port (socket) on the computer, also called the *centronics* port, and sometimes labelled LPT1 (short for Line Printer 1). The connecting cable will contain a number of parallel wires, and may take the form of a *ribbon cable*, so called because it is flat and wide, like a ribbon.

Some printers are designed to receive data 'in serial' from the computer, i.e. one bit at a time. These have to be connected to the serial port (socket) on the computer, also called the RS-232 port, and sometimes labelled COM1 (short for Communications 1). This is the port used by the computer to communicate with other computers.

Computer printers also differ in other respects:

● there are character printers (which print one character at a time), line printers (which print a line at a time), and page printers (which print a page at a time)
● a variety of printing technologies are possible, the main ones being dot matrix, daisy wheel, and laser
● some printers can handle only text, whereas others can handle text and graphics
● there are a variety of standards for *control codes*, which are commands sent from the computer to the printer to turn on effects such as underlining and emboldening.

However, most software packages are able to cope with these differences. They do so by means of *printer drivers*, special programs which adapt the output from the software to the printer. All you have to do is to select your printer's name from the list that is presented to you when you first use the software.

The main types of printer are described below. The main differences between them are:

● their quality of output
● whether they are able to print graphics
● their print speed
● their purchase price.

Dot matrix printers

These are inexpensive, relatively fast, and versatile, and therefore very popular. The print mechanism consists of a matrix of tiny needles. By hitting selected needles so that they stand out from the rest, the printer is able to create the shape of a letter or other character, which is then transferred to the paper via an inked ribbon. The print speed is typically 100 characters per second or more, and these printers are able to produce double size or very small characters, or bold print, italics, or other effects. They are also able to print pictures or graphs, if used with graphics software.

However, the print quality is not all that high, since the characters are not perfectly formed but consist of a pattern of dots. The resolution of most dot matrix printers is around 100 to 150 dots per inch. To overcome this defect, many dot matrix printers offer a *near letter quality* (NLQ) mode. When in this mode, the print head prints each line twice, the second pass slightly offset from the first, which has the effect of filling in the gaps between the holes and making the characters more perfectly formed. This gives results which, although not of the highest quality, are acceptable for most correspondence.

One of the earliest and most popular dot matrix printers for personal computers is the Epson FX-80. This has set a standard for control codes (for emboldening, graphics, etc.) which many other manufacturers of dot matrix printers have followed. Almost all software supports this standard, and nowadays you can buy an Epson-compatible for as little as £150.

A related type of printer is the *line-printer*, used in the data processing departments of large organizations for high-volume work. This is a much faster machine, and much more expensive. One version has up to 160 print wheels arranged in the form of a barrel, with characters embossed on each wheel, and able therefore to print up to 160 characters (a complete line) simultaneously. The quality is similar to that of the dot-matrix printer, but no NLQ mode is provided.

Ink-jet printers

Like dot matrix printers, these create the shape of characters from a pattern of dots on the paper, but in this case the dots are created by squirting particles of ink from a fine jet. The quality is higher than that of dot matrix printers, almost as good as laser printers (see below), and being non-impact they are much quieter. Colour ink-jets are also available.

Ink-jets have recently come down in price, and they now compete directly with better-quality dot matrix models. They are therefore likely to increase their share of the market in the future.

Daisy wheel printers

The print head in this type of printer is a *daisy wheel*, a circular device with a diameter of 3 inches which resembles a daisy flower. The print characters are embossed on the tip of each 'stalk'. When printing, the wheel rotates to bring the required character uppermost, and a hammer strikes it against an ink or carbon ribbon and so produces the printed impression on the paper. The print quality is high, much better than that of dot matrix printers, and slightly superior to that of the current generation of desktop laser printers.

The cheaper daisy wheel printers cost about the same as the Epson FX-80 or equivalent dot matrix printers, but they are much slower, generally printing at 1J to 15 characters per second. A fast daisy wheel printer – that is, one printing 40 or 50 characters per second – will cost several times this amount.

Because the print head is made up of pre-formed embossed characters, this type of printer is not as versatile as the dot matrix variety. It cannot print graphics, and if you wish to change the type style from e.g. normal to italics, you have to change daisy wheels.

Laser printers

Laser-beam printers, commonly called laser printers, are page printers, meaning that they print an entire page at a time. In fact they resemble photocopiers in size and appearance (see Figure 3.3), and employ a similar technology. They are very fast, typical speeds being around 8 pages per minute, and virtually silent in operation.

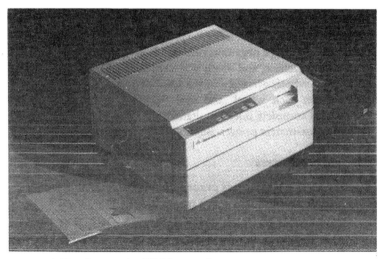

Figure 3.3 The Centronics PP-8 laser printer

The print quality is good, almost equal to that of daisy wheel printers. The resolution of current models is 300 dots per inch (dpi), though some of the latest versions offer 600 dpi. Most laser printers can handle graphics as well as text.

They therefore offer the quality of the daisy wheel with the versatility of the dot matrix, while being faster and quieter than either. The print quality is higher than that of ink-jet printers, but they are more expensive.

The print mechanism in a laser printer consists of a laser light, rollers, and ink, and works as follows. A sheet of paper is fed from a tray into the machine, and receives an electrostatic charge across its surface. The laser beam then rapidly and invisibly traces the computer's output (text or graphics) as a pattern of tiny dots on the paper, a process which removes the electrostatic charge from the points where the beam strikes the paper. The paper then receives a fine spray of ink across its surface, which adheres to the points with no charge but which is washed off the rest. After passing between rollers, the paper emerges, heated and dried, at the front of the machine.

Question

5 In your position as youth club leader, which type of printer is most suitable for your computer system? Jot down reasons for your answer.

Plotters

A plotter is an output device for producing hard-copy of a drawing or design done on a computer. It consists of a flat surface on which a piece of paper can be fixed, together with a moving arm to which a pen is attached. The pen reproduces on the paper the design that has been built up on the computer screen. By automatically replacing the pen by another from a bank of pens at the side of the surface the plotter is able to produce multi-coloured diagrams.

The price varies from a few hundred to several thousand pounds, the more expensive plotters permitting larger sheets of paper and working at higher speeds.

The benefits of computers

The proliferation of alternative types of computer hardware is a measure of the success of the computer. That success has arisen because the computer offers great benefits at a low price. Here's a brief description of these benefits under the headings of quantity, quality, and timeliness of output.

- *Quantity* With computers, we can produce so much more. As a writer, I have doubled my output by using a computer. This means that I can double my earnings, or enjoy increased leisure, or a mixture of both. This benefit has come because I no longer have to produce a handwritten draft (on paper), which I then type (onto paper), and then revise by typing again (onto paper). I now enter the original text directly into the computer, and revise it quickly and easily on the screen.
- *Quality* With computers, the appearance of our output may be better. In the case of my work, the days of sending material to publishers with crossings out and Tippexed corrections has gone – the final output is faultless in that respect. As well as this, my computer offers me writing-aids such as spelling checks, an electronic thesaurus to offer alternative words at the touch of a key, and a style checker. In other applications, computers carry out calculations and other tasks with great accuracy, giving an error-free output.
- *Timeliness* With computers, we can produce our output so much more quickly. In the case of a business, this may mean financial and other reports produced promptly, which can aid decision-making, or inquiries answered promptly, which can aid customer relations. In the case of this book, I can produce it at twice the speed, which means that it can be published earlier and therefore enjoy a longer life before going out of date.

The uses of computers

Some of the main uses, or *applications*, of computers, are as follows.
- *Word processing* With a computer, text that you type in can be easily altered on the screen, frequently-used text can be stored and called up when needed, documents can be quickly rearranged with different line lengths or line spacing, and names and addresses from a mailing-list can be incorporated in a standard document to

produce personalized letters. As well as this, spelling and writing-style aids are available, and some word processing packages allow you to incorporate graphics into your documents.

● *Record keeping* With a computer, records – such as name-and-address records, stock records, and purchasing records – can be stored and rapidly sorted, retrieved, or updated, and calculations to produce totals and other summary figures automatically and quickly performed.

● *Spreadsheets* Spreadsheets are tables of numerical data, and a computer can automatically carry out calculations on these tables, so that accounting information, cash-flow forecasts, statistical analyses, and so on are quickly and painlessly obtained.

● *Graphics* With a computer, straight lines, angles, and geometric shapes can be quickly and accurately drawn, and standard components stored and incorporated as desired into larger designs. A computer is also able to construct automatically a variety of charts and graphs from sets of numerical data, for example from a spreadsheet.

● *Animation* Some computers are able to assist the task of producing animated displays and films. In certain systems, the animator draws key pictures, and the computer is able to generate intermediate drawings which, when displayed rapidly in sequence, give the effect of continuous motion. Animated effects are widely used in computer games.

● *Music* When linked to electronic musical keyboards or other musical input devices, some computer systems are able to generate automatically a suitable accompaniment. Some systems can assist the composer in his task, by automatically creating musical score. The composer indicates the key notes, the computer produces the intermediate passages.

● *Process control* When linked to factory equipment, the computer can control processes. For example, in a chemicals factory, computers check reactions and mixtures, and automatically adjust the flows of chemicals into the process if variations occur.

Assignment 3

a Using an Ordnance Survey map or road atlas, choose a suitable spot for a summer camp, and:

(i) use a computer drawing or painting package to draw a route map to the site

(ii) use a computer word processing package to write a list of directions to the site.

You should save your work on disk, but you should hand in to your tutor a hard-copy output of both pieces of work.

b As camp organizer, list the tasks that you think you would use a computer for (such as maintaining a mailing-list and writing letters, keeping the camp accounts, and producing graphics for posters or presentations), and state the benefits that you think would arise in each case from using a computer.

Recap

● The main input devices are the *keyboard* for typed input, the *mouse* for pointing, picking, and drawing, *optical character readers* to input previously typed text, the *microphone* for voice input, and *video cameras* and *scanners* for image input.

● Devices such as disks are used for long-term mass storage of programs and data. *Floppy disks* hold relatively small amounts of data, but are cheap and can be used to transfer material between computer systems. *Hard disks* provide large amounts of storage– typically 20 or 40 Mbytes – immediately to hand, and give very fast access times. *Optical discs* can be used for applications involving hundreds of Mbytes of stored data.

● *Monochrome monitors* using cathode ray tube technology are suitable for office computing applications involving word processing, record keeping, and spreadsheets. These are inexpensive, and give a high-resolution display. For applications where colour is important, *RGB* monitors (also using CRTs) may be best. Portable computers use flat screen monitors, based on *liquid crystal display* technology in the case of battery-powered models, or *gas plasma* technology in the case of mains-powered models. LCD screens give relatively poor contrast, and are less pleasant to use than other types of display.

● For *hard copy* output, a variety of printers are available. The main types are *dot matrix*, *daisy wheel*, and *laser* printers. Dot matrix printers are cheap, relatively fast, and can print text or graphics, but the quality of reproduction is inferior to that of the other types of printer, and they are fairly noisy. Daisy wheel printers are also quite cheap, and they give a high-quality output for text and data, but they are slow, they cannot print graphics, and they are very noisy. Laser printers produce

71

high-quality text and graphics, they are very fast and almost silent, but they are expensive.

- Computers offer substantial benefits, including an increased *quantity* of output, a higher *quality*, and more *timely* output.
- Computer applications include *word processing*, *record keeping*, *spreadsheets*, *graphics*, *animation*, *music*, and *process control*.

Answers to questions

1 in outline, the tasks are
  a load the drawing software from disk into RAM
  b draw the route map, using the drawing aids provided
  c save the finished result to disk
  d print out the route map.

2 A verbal description of the route could be dictated to the computer system and printed. Also, a hand-drawn sketch map of the route could be scanned into the system, from which a neat result could be automatically produced. Alternatively, the relevant details from a road atlas could be scanned in and edited.

3 You probably cannot justify a hard disk in financial terms. A hard disk will be the most expensive item in a low-cost computer system, and unless you are going to be using a computer for several hours each day – which is unlikely – the savings in time over the life of the computer and the greater convenience will not be enough to offset the initial £300 cost.

4 It depends what you are going to be using your computer for. If it is to be used entirely for standard office applications, such as writing letters and keeping records, then a monochrome CRT monitor makes most sense, as this will be cheap and give the high resolution that you need for this kind of work. If an important use is for computer games in connection with the youth club, or for other applications that benefit from colour, then an RGB monitor is best. If you need a computer that you can take with you to camp, then you need a portable battery-powered job that incorporates an LCD screen.

5 A dot matrix printer with NLQ mode is cheap and versatile, and probably the most suitable, being able to produce acceptable quality for letters and to print graphics. A laser printer would be very nice to have, but at today's prices would be far too expensive.

4: Computer software

Objectives

After reading this chapter, you should be able to:
- outline the range of tasks performed by computer software and indicate how it performs these tasks
- identify some major issues confronted by computer software, including software reliability, declarative versus procedural languages, and explain in a simple way the benefits of object-oriented programming
- use, in an elementary way, a representative range of software, including software running in an environment such as Windows.

Scenario

Once you get a computer, you have to learn how to carry out tasks like formatting disks, copying and deleting files, and running software. You also have to choose the software you are going to use with your system, and start to apply it to your administrative and other tasks.

The importance of software

Computers are becoming more and more alike. This is especially so in the business micro world. (I am excluding home micros such as the Spectrum.) Like motor cars, they come in differently shaped boxes, and the contents of those boxes may differ slightly. But so far as you, the user, is concerned, they all behave in a similar way. They handle screens, disk–drives, and printers in what seems the same way, and most run the same or similar software.

If a fantastic new software product comes out on the Apple Macintosh, within a couple of years it will also be available on IBM-PCs and compatibles, the Atari ST, and others. Likewise successful products running on the PC are soon available on the Apple Mac. If you want to use the Lotus 1-2-3 spreadsheet package, or Microsoft's

Excel, or the WordPerfect word processor, or Microsoft's Word, to name but a few, then you can buy any of the machines I've mentioned. For most computer tasks, it makes little difference which hardware you buy – it's the software that counts.

And whatever the hardware merits of the Macintosh or the Atari ST, they do not have as much software available as the PC. Which is one reason why some 10 million PCs have been sold world-wide, compared to a fraction of that number for other makes. For example, although the Commodore Amiga is a remarkable machine, it has so little serious software available for it that few business people will touch it.

So newer micros, such as the Acorn Archimedes, provide PC emulators – software or hardware add-ons that make the machine behave just like a PC, able to run the PC's software. Some micros, such as the Atari ST, enable you to emulate several other machines. These emulators slow down the running speed considerably, but computers like the Archimedes are so fast that the performance is still acceptable. In fact, we cannot be many years away from the day when a single box will be able to emulate almost any other computer, and therefore to run almost any software that you care to buy.

What is software?

So what is computer software? It is programs of computer instructions, stored on magnetic disk, semiconductor ROM, or other suitable storage devices. To run a program, the computer loads it from the storage device into RAM, and the instructions it contains are then executed by the CPU. In the case of computers based upon conventional microprocessors, the instructions are executed serially, i.e. one after another. In the case of computers based upon the newer transputer, many of the instructions are executed in parallel, i.e. at the same time.

The computer needs software to tell it how to carry out its various tasks:

- it needs *system software* to carry out *housekeeping* tasks like formatting disks, copying files from one disk to another, and so on
- it needs *application software* to carry out its various applications, such as writing letters, keeping records, and producing drawings or charts.

I shall be describing both of these types of software later in this chapter.

Question

1 As the camp organizer for your youth club, what tasks might you want to carry out on a computer system? Jot down a list – you will use this in later activities.

How software works

An instruction contained in a computer program takes the form of a sequence of bits (binary 0s and 1s). When the instruction is executed, these bits travel as electrical pulses to the CPU. Here, logic gates contained in special control circuits make these bits close switches in a second circuit along which the computer data flows. In this way the program operates on data.

This is represented diagrammatically in Figure 4.1. Each type of action that the computer can perform – such as addition, subtraction, or a logical operation – has associated with it a particular set of logic

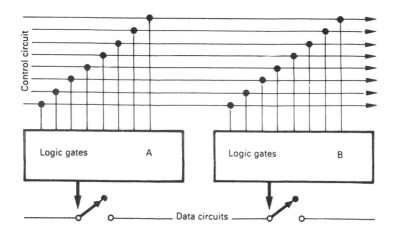

Figure 4.1 A control circuit in a computer

gates. The bits flowing down the control circuit pass each set of logic gates, but only one set will output a current and so close a switch.

Programming languages

In the early days of computing, programmers wrote these instructions as sequences of 0s and 1s. This is called *machine code*, as it is the code or *language* that the machine understands. A program to carry out even quite a simple task consists of many machine code instructions, and so program-writing in the early days was very time consuming and arduous. Machine code is sometimes called the *first generation* programming language.

To simplify matters and speed up the task of programming, *assembly languages* were developed. These were one stage removed from machine code in the direction of human-understandability, and are sometimes called *second generation* programming languages. With these, programmers could write instructions in an easier form, using commands such as: LDA, meaning *load accumulator*; ADC, meaning *add with carry*; and CLC, meaning *clear carry*. The assembly language converts these commands into the strings of 0s and 1s that the computer understands.

Although these commands take away the need to know anything about the sequence of bits that must be sent to the control circuit, they still demand a good knowledge of what goes on inside the computer in order to perform even simple tasks such as addition or subtraction. For example, you need to know that numbers to be added or subtracted have to be loaded into the accumulator (a special area of working memory in the CPU), and you have to tell the computer to carry numbers when performing addition. Here is the sequence of assembly language commands for adding 2 and 2 on computers which use the 6502 microprocessor (used in computers such as the BBC). An explanation is given at the right of each command.

```
LDA #&2 /Put the number 2 into the accumulator
CLC      /Clear carry before addition
ADC #&2/Add 2 to the contents of the accumulator
STA &70  /Store the result in memory location &70
```

Because in both machine code and assembly language you are working close to the level of the computer and require an intimate knowledge of the way in which it works, they are called *low-level languages.* Furthermore, since these languages are addressing the actual circuitry inside the CPU, they are machine-dependent, meaning that they vary from one type of computer to another. So computers based on the 6502 microprocessor use a different assembly language to PCs which are based on the Intel 8086 family of micro-processors.

Nowadays, most programming is done in *high-level languages.* They are called this because they are a further level away from the level of the machine, and their commands are such that you don't need to know anything about the computer's circuitry in order to write programs. The commands are, in fact, fairly close to the language of ordinary English and arithmetic. For example, to add 2 and 2 in many high-level languages, you simply type in: 2 + 2. This not only makes programming easier, it means that programs written in these languages are not restricted to particular types of microprocessor. In theory, such a program will run on any computer, though some modifications may be required to cope with hardware differences, e.g. screen display variations. In practice, some languages, notably BASIC, vary somewhat from computer to computer, and BASIC programs written for one may require extensive modifications before they will run on another.

Although programs in high-level languages are relatively easy for humans to write, they are not directly comprehensible to the computer, which needs detailed instructions in the form of binary 0s and 1s. So the computer must translate these commands into its low-level language.

With some high-level languages, this translation job takes place while the program is being run. This means that the computer has to translate commands and execute them at the same time, which slows the program down. This type of translation is called *interpretation* and is carried out by a piece of system software called an *interpreter*. The most well-known interpreted language is BASIC. Interpreted languages require relatively small amounts of computer memory to run, one reason why BASIC became so popular on microcomputers, which used to have severely limited amounts of RAM.

With most high-level languages, however, the program is trans-lated before it is run. This type of translation is called *compilation*, and is carried out by a piece of software called a *compiler*. A program that has been translated is said to be *compiled*. It is then run in its compiled form.

Well-known compiled languages are COBOL and C, both of which are standardized across a wide range of machines. COBOL is mainly used on large computers, and is the language of data processing, and C is used across a range of computers including microcomputers. A program written in C can be compiled for a variety of different computers, and then sold in its compiled form for those computers.

Many hundreds of programming languages exist, each with their strengths and weaknesses. Three of the most widely used are FORTRAN, BASIC and COBOL, and these are described briefly below.

FORTRAN

The development of FORTRAN was started by IBM in 1954, and it was first put to use in that organization in 1957. FORTRAN is short for FORmula TRANslation and, as this name implies, it was designed for engineering, statistics, and other mathematically oriented applications. It is good at carrying out complex calculations, which can be coded as compressed statements much like ordinary mathematical formulae. It requires a large compiler, which limited its use to computers with reasonably large amounts of memory.

Being almost the first high-level language, FORTRAN became firmly entrenched as the language for scientific use, and it still retains that position. BASIC, the most popular language of all for general-purpose use, was derived from FORTRAN.

A program written in FORTRAN consists of a list of numbered statements, called program lines, which express in a compact form a sequence of instructions to the computer. There are four kinds of statement, which we can think of as analogous to the four kinds of task – control, arithmetic/logic, input and output – that go on in a computer system (see the start of Chapter 2):

● Control statements.
● Arithmetic statements.
● Input statements.
● Output statements.

Control statements tell the computer how to sequence its execution of the program. Normally, the program lines will be executed in numbered order, but if in line 50 there is the control statement

GOTO 100, the computer will branch straight to line 100, missing all the intervening program lines. This does not mean that those program lines are unnecessary; the GOTO statement may be an option that is executed only if a certain state of affairs exists, such as a value being more than a certain amount. Testing for certain conditions, and then branching on the results of the tests, is a very important part of most programs.

Arithmetic statements govern the calculations that take place when the program is run. In FORTRAN, these are similar to the statements of ordinary arithmetic, using plus $(+)$, minus $(-)$, multiplication $(*)$, division $(/)$, powers and brackets in the usual way. For example, to calculate the total price T of N items which cost £P each, with VAT at 15% added on, the statement might be written like this:

$$T = N*P*1.15$$

Input and output statements govern the input of data into the computer and the output of the results. For example, the statement

READ (5,N,P)

would tell the computer to read from device 5 (which would be some form of input device) the values given to N and P.

BASIC

Short for 'Beginners All-purpose Symbolic Instruction Code', BASIC was developed in the early 1960s at Dartmouth College in America as a simplified version of FORTRAN, the intention being to produce a language for teaching the principles of programming. In the early days it was a simple language, with limited use outside education, but owing to its frugal memory requirements it was adopted as the main programming language for microcomputers. Many additional commands and structures were then added to extend the language's capabilities, each microcomputer manufacturer developing their own version of BASIC.

These extensions put BASIC on a par with FORTRAN for mathematical and scientific work. However, FORTRAN was designed in the days when computers were limited in power and expensive, and so an important requirement was that it carried out its tasks efficiently and in a way that made frugal demands on the computer's power. BASIC is not a particularly efficient language, but this hardly matters now that computing power is so cheap and plentiful. Ease of use and a short learning time are more important for people who are learning programming.

Besides being designed for beginners, BASIC was intended to be 'all-purpose'. Indeed, it can be used with almost any application, from performing scientific calculations to keeping business records and controlling devices such as robot arms. However, being a general-purpose language, it is not as good for specific applications as the more specialized languages such as FORTRAN and COBOL.

Figure 4.2 shows a short program written in BASIC. When run, it allows the user to input the unit price of a product, which it stores in memory under the variable PRICE, then input the quantity sold of the product, which it stores in memory under the variable QUANTITY. It then calculates the value of the sale, the VAT, and the total amount, displaying the results on the screen. The program repeats this sequence endlessly until the user enters nothing as the price, i.e. simply presses the RETURN/ENTER key. It is quite easy to entend this program so that it produces proper invoices.

```
10   REPEAT
20   INPUT "Enter the description" D$
30   INPUT "Enter the unit price" P
40   INPUT "Enter the number sold" N
50   LET A = P * N
60   PRINT "The amount for this sale is £"; A
70   PRINT "The VAT is £"; A * 0.15
80   PRINT "The amount including VAT is £"; A * 1.15
90   UNTIL D$ =""
```

Figure 4.2 A simple BASIC program

Activity

You probably have access to a BBC microcomputer, or perhaps a computer such as an RM Nimbus that runs BBC BASIC. If so, type in the program shown in Figure 4.2 and RUN it.

COBOL

COBOL is an acronym for COmmon Business Oriented Language. It was developed in 1960, at the initiative of the US

Defense Department, to provide a language that was efficient at file-handling and which could therefore be applied to business-oriented applications such as stock control. One of its earliest uses was the control of inventory on US warships.

With its file-handling capabilities, COBOL quickly established itself as the major language for processing business data, and it still retains this lead in organizations which use large computers.

A COBOL program consists of four divisions. These are:

● The *identification* division, which contains information for the users of the program, but which does not affect the processing of the data.
● The *environment* division, which specifies the hardware environment – i.e. the computer system and associated devices – in which the program will run.
● The *data* division, which specifies the files to be used, the type and size of data entries, and the computer storage required.
● The *procedure* division, which lists the operations that have to be performed by the computer to process the data, such as instructions to open files, to transfer data from those files to the computer's memory, to perform calculations, and to output results.

To illustrate these operations, here's a short extract from the procedure division of the COBOL program:

```
1 -OPEN-FILES.
   OPEN INPUT IN-FILE.
   OPEN OUTPUT OUT-FILE.

2 -SET-RECORDS.
   MOVE SPACES TO OUT-REC.
   MOVE 1 TO 0-RECORD-TYPE.

3 -READ-FILE-IN.
   READ IN-FILE AT END GO TO 5-FINISH,
   ADD 1 TO WS-COUNT-IN.
   MOVE IN-COPY TO OUT-COPY-1.
   READ IN-FILE AT END GO TO 8-ABORT.
   ADD 1 TO WS-COUNT-IN.
   MOVE IN-COPY TO OUT-COPY-2.
```

Software reliability

The languages we have discussed so far are called *procedural* languages, because they involve writing down the procedures (lists of steps) that we wish the computer to carry out to achieve our requirements. This type of language involves a considerable risk of programming errors, as fallible human programmers find it very difficult to get such procedures 100% correct. These errors (or *bugs*) lead to huge delays in implementing programs, and add enormously to the time and the cost required to produce software.

Look at the following statistics, which illustrate the seriousness of the situation:

● program testing and debugging takes 50% of the time of a software development project
● when a major piece of software is released, there are typically 5 errors for every 100 program statements
● even if the Star Wars software under development is the US is 100 times better than that of the average system, it would still have 100 000 errors.

The branch of computer science called *software engineering* has developed disciplines and techniques aimed at cutting down on programming errors and introducing a more scientific methodology into program production. In particular, it is shifting the emphasis away from the use of procedural languages towards what are known as *declarative languages*, and it has encouraged the use of more formal methods in specifying what programs should achieve. We look briefly at these in the next sections.

Program specification

Before work starts on programming a major piece of software, a *specification* of what the software should do must be written down. This is the task of systems analysis and design, discussed in Chapter 7. Traditionally, this specification has been written down in ordinary English. The result has been huge documents containing many ambiguities, and these have led to programs which not only contain errors but which have not always achieved precisely what the system designers had in mind when they drafted the specification.

Because of these problems, much more formal specification methods have been introduced, involving mathematical methods of specifying what programs should achieve. The resulting specifications look more like mathematical equations than English sentences. These equations can then be tested for correctness using mathematical proofs, before a single line of program code has been written. This development has been coupled with the appearance of new types of programming language which are not very far removed from the language of the specification, so that it is a relatively straightforward and error-free task to translate the specification into program code.

Although offering a solution to the problems of long program development time and widespread errors, these techniques have not as yet been widely adopted as the majority of systems analysts and computer programmers do not currently have the required levels of mathematical expertise. This will change though as software engineering becomes more firmly established in the computing community.

There are two main (mathematical) languages used for writing down specifications. One is called Z, the other VDM.

Declarative languages

The specifications discussed above state *what* the program should do, not *how* it should do it. Procedural programming languages are very much concerned with translating the *what* into the *how*. Wouldn't it be nice, though, if you could tell the computer what to do, and *it* decided how to do it? This is precisely the aim of some modern programming languages.

These are called *declarative* languages, because they allow you to concentrate on declaring in a precise way the purpose of your program, so avoiding getting bogged down in the procedures involved in achieving that intention. This means that programming is moving towards restating the intentions of the systems designer, as expressed in a formal specification, into the code of the particular language being used. And since the formal specification will have been tested mathematically to prove its correctness, the possibility of errors in the final program code should be minimized.

Declarative languages fall into the following categories:

- Functional programming languages, such as ML and Miranda, which view programming intentions as mathematical functions.
- Logic programming languages, such as Prolog, based on a branch of mathematics called *predicate logic*. In these, the programming intention is expressed as a statement which is to be proved true.
- Object-oriented languages, such as Eiffel and Smalltalk. In these, real-world objects such as bank accounts are self-contained pieces (modules) of computer code, and computations are carried out by passing messages between the objects. *How* the objects compute the message is of no consequence to the program developer, it's *what* they do with them that counts.

Object-oriented programming offers many advantages over other programming methods, and object-oriented methods are finding their way into traditional procedural languages. For instance, C++ is a modern version of the widely used programming language C with object-oriented extensions, and Modula-2 and Ada are descendants of Pascal offering object-oriented features. Because of its importance, a brief description of the principles of object-oriented programming is given below.

Object-oriented languages

Object-oriented languages aim to improve the quality and correctness of programs, and reduce their cost, by adopting the following principles:

- *Modularity* – programs must be broken down into separately compilable modules, which correspond to the objects in the real world that the program is addressing such as customer accounts. The internal structure of the module is of no consequence to the user and should be hidden; all that matters is its *interface*, that is, the services it offers, i.e. the operations it performs on the messages (or data) received from other modules. Note that all objects of a particular type are called a *class*. So customer accounts form a class, and an instance of a class, such as the account of one particular customer, is an *object*.
- *Messages* – classes are agents that communicate with each other by sending messages (data). The internal structure of the class,

i.e. its program code, must be such as enable it to respond to messages sent to it.

● *Inheritance* – classes form hierarchies with *ancestors* and *descendants*. For example, the class 'accounts' may have as its descendants 'customer accounts', 'supplier accounts' and so on, and customer accounts may have as descendants 'credit customers' 'cash-only customers', etc. Descendant classes are able to call upon the services offered by ancestor classes as well as offering services of their own. When an object receives a message, if it does not contain the code enabling it to respond to the message it forwards the message up the ancestor chain until a class which is able to respond to it is found.

The inheritance mechanism means that software design investment can be used over and over again; descendant classes are able to call upon the services offered by their ancestors rather than incorporate those services into their own structure. And the fact that classes are separately compilable program modules means that they can be re-used time and again by different software. What this means is that a piece of software produced in an object-oriented programming language will consist of a relatively small main program which calls upon various objects held in a library of modules. These objects will have been thoroughly tested and debugged by their repeated use in other software.

System software

Let's now turn to the various kinds of computer software that are available, beginning with system software. This can be split into the following categories:

● *operating systems*, which control the disk–drives and other hardware devices, and which allow you to load, copy, and delete files, and carry out other computer housekeeping tasks
● *operating environments*, which provide an easy-to-use way of carrying out operating system tasks
● *utilities*, which provide additional facilities and routines.

We'll look at each of these three types of systems software in turn.

Operating systems

A computer's operating system enables it to carry out its disk filing and other operational tasks. We can put most of these tasks under four headings:

- *disk operations*, which are to do with storing programs and data on disk
- *network operations*, which enable a number of micros to be linked to each other and to share facilities such as hard disks and printers
- *multi-tasking*, which enables the computer to handle several tasks at the same time, such as running a record-keeping application, a spreadsheet, and a word-processing program
- *multi-user operations*, which allow a number of people to use the computer and its software at the same time, by connecting to it other PCs or workstations.

At the time of writing, most operating systems on microcomputers are able to handle only the first of these groups of tasks, namely disk operations. Computers based on the Intel 8086 family of micro processors (i.e. IBM PCs and PC-compatibles) use an operating system called *DOS*, short for *disk operating system*. In the case of the IBM PC, its full name is *PC-DOS*, short for *personal computer disk operating system*; in the case of the compatible PCs from other manufacturers, its full name is *MS-DOS*, the MS being short for Microsoft, the software house that wrote DOS. In spite of the differences in name, the two products are, for most practical purposes, identical.

DOS was developed from the earlier *CP/M* operating system used on Z80-based microcomputers. Few Z80 computers are now made, the most well-known current example being the Amstrad PCW word processor.

Over the years, DOS has grown steadily more powerful, and has passed through several versions or *levels*. Each version has added features which support new hardware developments, such as the ability to handle hard disks, 3.5-inch disks, and so on. The current version is level 5. The version designed for the new IBM PS/2 microcomputers is called OS/2, and this supports multi-tasking as well as multi-user applications.

Digital Research Corporation, which is Microsoft's main competitor, sells a competing operating system for PCs called

Concurrent DOS. At the time of writing, this offers the following features:

- multi-tasking with up to four *windows* visible at any time on the screen, each running a different program
- multi-user facilities for up to three users, using PCs or workstations linked to an IBM-AT or compatible
- compatibility with DOS, so that programs written for that operating system will run without difficulty.

A more powerful operating system, which runs on larger computers and also high-end PCs is *Unix*. This is designed with multi-tasking and multi-user applications in mind, and is steadily increasing in popularity as microcomputers become more powerful and more capable of operating in these modes. It is worth noting that the *Helios* operating system being developed for the new generation of transputer-based computers is based upon Unix.

Other types of computer use different operating systems. In the microcomputer world, for example, the 68020-based Atari ST uses the *TOS* operating system, and the 6502-based BBC Micro uses Acorn's *DFS*, short for *disk filing system.*

Question

2 In recent years personal computer users have become increasingly keen on multi-tasking. Think about the kind of use that is made of PCs in offices – for example the office tasks that you, the youth club leader/camp organizer have to carry out – and jot down three ways in which you think multi-tasking will help.

How the operating system organizes the disk

Storing, organizing, and retrieving files are central tasks for all operating systems. To understand these systems, it is therefore necessary to know something of the principles of disk filing.

Each file, whether it is a program file supplied by a software house or a data or text file that you have produced, is given a name. That name, together with the location of the file on the disk, is stored in the index, a special area on the disk's surface. When you type the filename, the operating system looks it up in the index, locates the file, and loads it into RAM.

Directories

Because a hard disk can hold many hundreds or thousands of files, it is necessary to organize them into separate sections in the index. These sections are called *directories*, and they act rather like the sections in a library, separating files by subject matter or use. For example, the word processing software that you use may be held in one directory, and your record-keeping software in another. The text or data files that you create may be held in the same directories as the software, or you may find it convenient to house them in other directories.

(Floppy disks have only a small storage capacity in comparison and can therefore hold only a relatively small number of files. In this case it is not essential to organize the files into directories, and operating systems that were developed before hard disks appeared – such as CP/M – are not able to handle directories.)

Directories are organized into what's called a *tree structure*. To appreciate what this means, think of a directory as the branch of a tree:

● as a branch has leaves, so a directory has files
● as a branch splits off into smaller branches which have their own leaves, so a directory may contain other subdirectories, each with its own files.

The basic directory which contains all other directories is called the *root* directory.

Figure 4.3 shows part of the directory structure of my hard disk. As you can see, I've called one of the directories QA, as this contains Q&A, the software package that I mostly use for word processing and record keeping. This directory contains two subdirectories called DATA and TEXT; these hold the data files (for the record-keeping part of Q&A) and the text files (for the word processing part) respectively. Because I have so many text files, I find it convenient to have several subdirectories within TEXT, to separate out letters, files created by my wife, and so on. These are shown in the figure.

Naming files

To distinguish individual files within a directory, they must be given unique names. In many operating systems, including DOS, a filename consists of two parts: the *stem* (the main part of the name) and an *extension*, separated by a dot. In CP/M and DOS, the stem can be up to 8 characters long, and the extension up to 3 characters long. The stem can be used to identify the contents of the file, the extension can be used to identify what type or class of file it is.

For example, I have called the file containing this chapter of text CHAP4.IT

The stem identifies it as Chapter 4, the extension identifies it (to me) as part of this IT book.

In the case of program files, the operating system dictates what the extension should be:

● in DOS and CP/M you can write your own batch program files to execute batches of operating system commands automatically (see your operating system manual), and you must give these the extension BAT
● some system files (i.e. files which are connected with the operating system) must have the extension SYS
● some program files must have the extension COM (short for command)
● other program files must have the extension EXE (short for executable).

To run BAT, SYS, COM, and EXE files you can omit the extension and merely type the stem of the name. If there is a file of that name on the disk with one of these extensions, DOS or CP/M will run it.

Activity

Look at the list of tasks that you produced in answer to Question 1 at the start of this chapter, and design a suitable directory structure to hold the software and data/text files for these tasks on a hard disk. For help with this activity, study Figure 4.3.

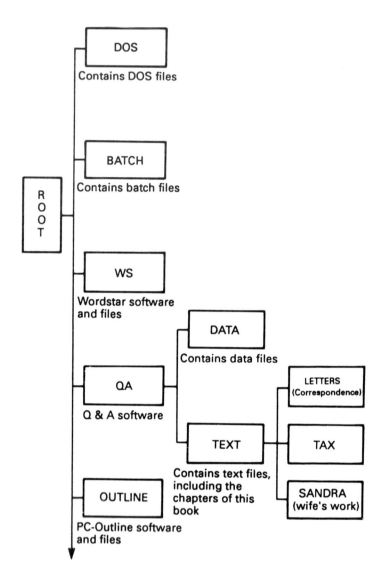

Figure 4.3 Part of the directory system on big hard disk

Operating system commands

Although operating systems differ in their capabilities, some offering more facilities than others, they all perform the same types of tasks. Furthermore, they often use similar commands, examples being the command COPY to copy a file, DEL to delete a file, and RENAME to rename a file. Others are MD to make a directory and CD to change directories. In the case of program file, you simply type the file name in order to run it.

Some other common commands are:

A:

to get the computer to look at drive A (normally the first floppy disk drive), and

C:

to make the hard disk drive (normally drive C) the currently accessed drive.

DIR

will, on DOS-based systems, tell the computer to display the contents of the current directory.

Activity

If you have access to a computer that can handle directories, use its operating system to set up the directory system (or part of the directory system) that you designed in the last activity. However, don't at this point copy any files into your directories.

Operating environments

DOS and most other operating systems are not 'user-friendly'. Their commands are awkward to memorize and use, and if you are not familiar with the computer keyboard they are awkward to type. Also, the computer screen with its enigmatic C:\> is rather unfriendly and difficult to come to terms with, and most people appreciate something that resembles more closely the familiar world of the office with its drawers, folders, wastepaper basket, and so on.

Hence the need for *operating environments*, software which sits on top of the operating system and presents us with an easy-to-use and friendly way of performing the kinds of tasks described above. The two most popular operating environments on microcomputers are:

1 The Apple Macintosh operating environment and the almost identical *GEM* from Digital Research. GEM is short for 'Graphics Environment Manager', and it is available on the Atari ST, PC-compatibles, and some other micros.
2 *Windows* from Microsoft, available for all PC-compatibles, though best used on 80386 models and above. This is virtually identical to *Presentation Manager* (PM), used on the IBM PS/2 range of micros.

Both the Macintosh/GEM environment and Windows/PM have many similarities, for they are both based on the earlier operating environment developed by Xerox at the end of the 1970s. In the future, this way of working is likely to become common across computers of every kind.

Xerox's original product – which was never released commercially – grew out of painstaking research into the way in which people interact with computers. Pressing the arrow keys on the keyboard to move around the screen, for instance, is not very efficient or natural, and so the mouse was developed. Pushing this across your desk produces corresponding movements of the cursor on the screen. Selecting files or software options by typing at the keyboard is also unnatural and inefficient, so a button is provided at the front of the mouse. Now, to make your selection, you merely push the mouse to move to the file or the option displayed on the screen, and click the button. In the case of a software program, you run it by 'double clicking', i.e. pressing the button twice in quick succession.

Xerox's research also showed that most people find the conventional text-based display unfriendly and difficult to use, preferring instead one that was graphics based. In this, pictures or *icons* represent the functions and tasks of the system, examples being a picture of a wastepaper basket to represent the delete function for getting rid of files, a filing drawer to represent a disk-drive, and so on. The cursor itself is represented by an icon, normally an arrow to point to files or functions.

Even files are represented by icons, namely miniature sheets of paper containing the filenames, and directories are represented by pictures of folders. The contents of a directory appear in a box or 'window' on the screen. Several directories can be displayed at the same time in different windows, and files can be copied from one to another simply by selecting them with the mouse, keeping the button held down, and 'dragging' them to another window.

Other facilities include:

● *Pull-down menus.* The menus are listed across the top of the screen, and a menu's options appear as a list below it when you point to it with the mouse. To select an option, you point and click with the mouse.

● *Dialogue boxes.* These appear in situations where you need to turn a number of options on or off, or type in something like a filename. To set an option, you mouse-click on a 'radio button' located alongside it (Figure 4.4).

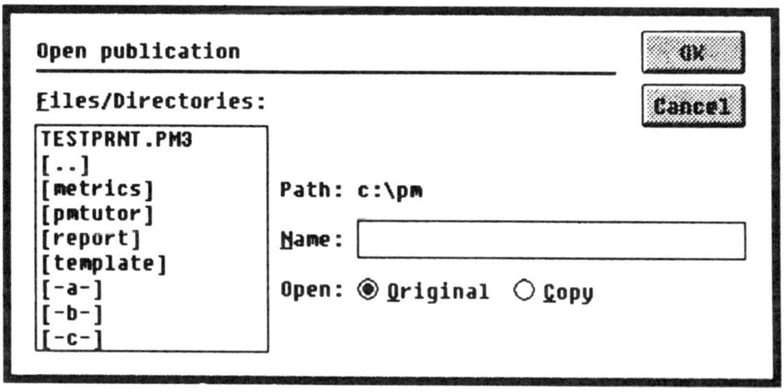

Figure 4.4 Example of a dialogue box

This kind of interface is called a *graphical user interface*, or GUI. The term WIMP is also used, meaning 'Window, Icon, Mouse, Pointer'.

Windows

Early versions of Windows were much inferior to the Mac/GEM environment, and little application software was written to take advantage of this environment. With version 3, released in 1990, Windows has become a fully fledged graphical user interface. Its desktop somewhat resembles the Mac/GEM Desktop, with scroll bars, pull-down menus, icons, dialogue boxes, etc. The virtually identical product for the PS/2, Presentation Manager, appeared a couple of years earlier.

Although it arrived late on the scene, Windows 3 is much more powerful than GEM, as it overcomes the two main limitations of (the current version of) the PC's operating system, DOS:

● It breaks the 640K memory barrier, allowing Windows applications to use up to 32 Mb.
● It provides multi-tasking facilities, i.e. it can run several applications at the same time, each within a different window. This multi-tasking capability is very potent, for it allows you to switch instantly from one task to another, to copy data rapidly from one to another, and to carry out one job while another is being processed in the background.

Note that these facilities are only fully available on PCs using the 80386 processor and above. PCs with lower specifications can use only some of the power of Windows. In addition, Windows may run so slowly on cheaper machines that it loses its appeal. (Alternative operating environments are available for low-cost PCs – see later in this chapter.)

Windows also offers a number of other powerful features, including *Dynamic Data Exchange* (DDE). This allows data to be copied from one Windows application to another, and the link that is thus created between the two applications kept 'live'. This means that if the data is changed in one application, these changes are automatically updated in the other.

Using Windows

In the next activity I'm going to ask you to make use of Windows running on a PC (or similar environments such as that of the Apple

Computer software

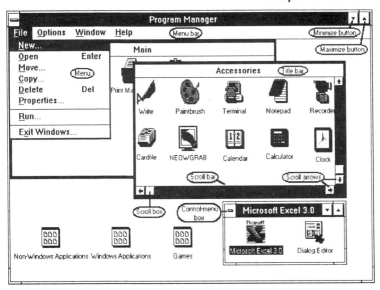

Figure 4.5 The Windows environment running Program Manager

Mac). This section, which explains the main features of Windows, should help with this.

Figure 4.5 shows the Windows Program Manager up and running on my computer. (Normally, when you run Windows, this is the application that initially and automatically appears.) I've marked on this figure a number of the Windows features listed below. The accompanying text explains how to make use of these features using the mouse.

Using the keyboard rather than the mouse is less intuitive and generally more awkward, and to keep the explanation simple I'm assuming you will not want to do this. However, if you don't have a mouse, the keyboard alternatives are explained in the Basic Skills chapter of the *Microsoft Windows User's Guide*. However, some keystroke alternatives to the mouse are quick and easy shortcuts, and these are described below.

● *Workspace.* This is the area of the screen occupied by an application, where you do your work. In Figure 4.5 the current application is the Windows Program Manager, and the

95

workspace is the whole of its window, which, as you can see, contains several document windows and some icons.

● *The menu bar.* Application windows have menu bars below their top border. In the figure, you can see the menu bar for Program Manager. (The menu bars for two Windows applications, namely Excel and Paintbrush, are shown in Figure 4.6.) Menu bars for different Windows applications all have a similar look and feel. For example, the 'File' menu is always at the left of the bar, the 'Help' menu is always at the right. To open a menu, simply point to its name with the mouse and click the left button. If you use the keyboard, hold down the Alt key and tap the underlined letter of the menu name – so to open the 'File' menu, press Alt and F. To close a menu without making a choice from it, point to its name again with the mouse and click, or else press the Esc key.

● *Menu option.* In Figure 4.5, the File menu is open. Again, the File menu for one Windows application will be similar to the File menu for another. For example, the 'New File' option will be at the top of this menu, and the 'Exit' option will be at the bottom. Choosing a menu option is much the same as choosing a menu from the menu bar: point to it with the mouse and click, or else press the underlined letter on the keyboard.

● *Window.* You will notice that several windows are open in the figure, each headed by a *title bar* naming the window's contents – e.g. 'Program Manager', or 'Accessories'. The window in which you are currently working is called the *active* window, and in the figure is indicated by the title in white text on a black background. In this case, Program Manager is the active application window, and within this the active document window is titled 'Microsoft Excel 3.0' – this contains icons for the Excel spreadsheet program and some related applications. An active window is always in the foreground, and may obscure other non-active windows. To make a window active, simply point anywhere within it with the mouse and click the left button. Alternatively, choose the Windows menu and then, from the list that appears, the title of the window you require.

● *Control-menu box.* Each active window has a control-menu box in the top-left corner. In the case of application windows, it is represented by a button marked by a spacebar symbol; in the case of document windows, by a button marked by a hyphen. If you *double click* on this button – i.e. point to it with the mouse and click twice – you will close the window and, if an application is running within it, the application as well. If you click once, a control menu appears, offering several options including one to alter the window's size (see below). Note the following keyboard alternatives: press Alt-space to open an application control menu, Alt-hyphen to open a document control menu, Alt-F4 to close the active application, Ctrl-F4 to close the active document.

● *Icon.* A number of icons are displayed in Figure 4.5. Some are *application icons,* representing individual applications such as 'Paintbrush', 'Notepad', and 'Microsoft Excel 3.0'. Others are *document icons,* and in the figure these are lists of program files, e.g. 'Games'. To run the program represented by an application icon, or display the contents of a document icon, point to it with the mouse and then double click, i.e. click the left button twice. This opens a window then runs the program or displays the document within it. Note that if you click once on an icon, you will open its control menu.

● *Maximize button.* An active window has this button in the top-right corner. It is marked by an upward-pointing arrow. When you click on it, the window expands to its maximum size, and may fill the entire screen. The maximize button is then replaced by a *restore* button (marked by an up and a down arrow); clicking on this restores the window to its former size.

● *Minimize button.* An active window also has a minimize button, marked by a downward-pointing arrow. When you click on this, the window is closed and reverts to an icon. If the window is running an application, that application is not closed. Instead, it remains in the background ready to run as soon as you double click on the application's icon.

● *Window border.* Borders surround the window on four sides, and in the figure you can see that these are represented by double lines in the case of active windows, and thick single lines in the case of non-active windows. You can alter the size of a window by pointing to a border, holding down the left button, and dragging with the mouse. If you do this at a window corner, you can alter the size in two directions at the same time. If you wish to move a window (without altering its size), point to the title bar and *drag* it to the desired position (by holding down the mouse button while moving the mouse).

● *Scroll bar.* Document windows have these, and they allow you to *scroll* (move) parts of the document into view which are currently beyond the window borders. The Accessories window in Figure 4.5 has scroll bars at the right and the bottom. If a document window does not have scroll bars, that's because it is large enough to show all its contents.

● *Scroll box.* Each scroll bar has a scroll box, and by dragging on this with the mouse you can scroll the document through the window. The position of the box on the bar indicates the position of the window relative to the document as a whole. For example, the position of the box in the bottom scroll bar in the Accessories window in Figure 4.5 shows that the window is at the extreme left of the document. The position of the scroll box in the vertical scroll bar at the right shows that the window is at the foot of the document.

● *Scroll arrows.* These are the buttons at the ends of the scroll bars. They provide a further means of scrolling the document through the window. Simply point to a scroll button and click to move a short way in the obvious direction; or keep the mouse button pressed down for repeated moves.

● *Dialogue box.* To see an example turn to Figure 4.4 on page 93. A dialogue box may provide you with information, or it may allow you to type in information. For example, if you are using Paintbrush and wish to open a picture stored on disk, you use the File Open dialogue box to type or select the file name. A dialogue box may contain *command buttons* that you click to initiate an action, *text boxes* in which you type information, *list boxes* to choose from a list of names (by clicking on your choice), *option buttons* which you can click to select from a number of mutually exclusive items, and *check boxes* to turn options on and off. The dialogue box in Figure 4.4 contains command buttons, option buttons, a list box, and a text box.

Comprehensive on-screen help on Windows is available – as you can see from Figure 4.5, 'Help' is one of the menus listed on the Program Manager menu bar. If you wish to find out more about Windows, you should spend some time exploring the help system – the next activity will get you started on this.

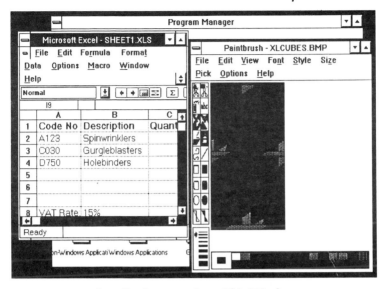

Figure 4.6 Several applications running within Windows

Activity

If you are new to Windows, practise using the features described above. Some suggested exercises are given below. When you have completed these exercises, you should use Program Manager to copy some files into some of the directories you set up in the last activity. If you don't have access to Windows running on PCs, use whatever is the equivalent environment on the computer you are using, such as the Apple Mac environment.

1 Run Windows, and if Program Manager does not automatically run, double click on its icon to activate it.

2 Open one or two of the document icons displayed in the Program Manager workspace, either by double clicking on their icons, or by choosing them from the Window menu. Practise closing Windows (by double clicking on their control-menu boxes), then opening them again.

3 Run the Paintbrush program by double clicking on its icon. (You will need to open the Accessories document window first to display its icon.)

4 Try using the File Open dialogue box within Paintbrush: choose the File menu, then the Open option, then scroll through the list of pictures that are displayed in its Files list box. Double click on one picture name to open it.

5 Close the Paintbrush program by double clicking on its control-menu box.

6 Practise altering the sizes of the windows that are now open on your screen, including maximizing, restoring, and minimizing them. Use the maximize/minimize/restore buttons, the window borders, and the window's control menu. Practise restoring any windows that you have minimized.

7 Try moving a window (by dragging its title bar).

8 Practise using scroll boxes and scroll arrows in a window. (If scroll arrows are not displayed in any windows on your computer, reduce a document window in size until they do appear.)

9 Have a look at the options in the various menus that are displayed in an application such as Program Manager or Paintbrush.

10 To get started with the Windows Help system, at the Program Manager menu bar choose Help then Index. Maximize the Help window that appears. From the menu bar in this window choose Help, then Using Help, work through the various Help Topics. Then click the Index button towards the top left of the window and choose Windows Help Index. Read through the topics of your choice listed here.

11 To get help on Program Manager, choose Program Manager Help Index (instead of Windows Help Index) in 10 above.

12 When you have finished with Help, double click on the Help window control-menu box.

Other environments for PCs

You can have multi-tasking, access to large amounts of memory, and a mouse-and-windows environment, without resorting to running Windows on a high-specification PC. One environment that will give you all these things and yet which will run on the lowliest 8086 machine is DesqView, from Quarterdeck.

DesqView is not a graphical user interface, so it does not use icons. It is character-based. The term COW (Character-Oriented Windows) is sometimes applied to software that is character-based but uses the mouse and windows. Like GUI environments, COW software includes devices such as pull-down menus and dialogue boxes from which you can make selections using the mouse. Its advantage over GUI software is the speed at which it runs, even on low-spec PCs.

GrandView, the package I am using for writing the second edition of this book, is COW software, and it's one of the fastest packages I've ever used. For ordinary tasks like writing text or keeping records there is little point in graphical user interface, as no graphics are involved. (If I were desktop publishing this book, however, I would want a GUI.) Another popular COW package is PC Tools (version 5 and above), from Central Point Software.

Utilities

The third category of system software is utilities. These enable you to extend the power of the operating system, by:

- carrying out tasks which are beyond the capabilities of the operating system
- carrying out operating system tasks in a more efficient and easier way.

Some utilities are designed to carry out one job only, such as restoring files that have been deleted in error. Others provide a computer housekeeping environment, enabling you to carry out housekeeping tasks as easily as in GEM or Windows, and from which you can run applications. The latter may include facilities which are lacking in GEM and Windows, such as options to hide files so that they cannot be altered or deleted, and so on.

However, unlike the Mac/GEM or Windows environments, you cannot run applications from within this type of software; you must run them from the operating system itself. All that this software does is provide an easy access to the operating system's facilities, together with a menu of some kind that enables you to run applications from within the operating system. For this reason they are called *front ends* (to the operating system) rather than environments. Popular front ends to DOS are PowerMenu, PC Tools, Qdos, and Xtree.

Application software

We've covered the main types of system software, so let's turn now to application software. This is the software that enables us to do the things that we bought our computer for, such as playing games, writing music, creating animated displays, or administering the office.

Application software is normally supplied as a *package*, consisting of:

● the software, supplied on one or more floppy disks
● a manual, explaining how to use the software
● training material, either supplied on disk, or in a booklet, or both.

IBM-PCs and compatibles (including ATs, 80386 machines, and PS/2s) are supported by thousands of software packages. Most of these are reasonably priced, and some are even free, being available in what is known as the *public domain*. Public domain (PD) software is normally available from user groups, the most important for the PC being Compulink at Guildford in Surrey. The manual in the case of a PD product is normally supplied as a text file on the same disk as the software, and has to be printed out by the user.

The Apple Macintosh is also well supported by application software, though not to the same extent as the PC. The Atari ST is also quite well supported, notably by games, graphics applications such as computer-aided design, and music.

The kinds of application packages that are available include:

● record-keeping software
● spreadsheet software
● word processing and desktop publishing software
● business graphics and presentations software
● communications software
● diary systems and other personal productivity tools
● expert systems software
● drawing and computer-aided design software
● games
● music synthesis
● painting and animation software.

Some packages can perform more than one of these tasks. For example, there are a number of office administration packages that will carry out word processing, record-keeping, spreadsheet work, and business graphics. These are called *integrated* packages, because they integrate, or bring together, these varied tasks. Some of them are remarkably cheap, one example for the PC being Ability, from Migent, costing just under £100. A more powerful integrated package which is very popular is Smart, which costs several hundred pounds, and is also available for the PC.

Features of application packages

Most application packages have the following features.

1 They may be *command-driven*, or *menu-driven*, or a combination of both. To illustrate what this means, DOS is command-driven, so that you have to learn a number of commands to use it, which you then type in. Windows and GEM, in contrast, are menu-driven, so that you merely have to select menu options to use their facilities. Command-driven software takes longer to learn, but gives you greater flexibility.

2 They often provide *context-sensitive help*. This means that by pressing a certain key – usually the function key F1 – a screen or more of text appears that gives guidance on the option you have selected or the task you are carrying out.

3 When using them, you normally create a file of data, text, or graphics, which you will want to save on disk for use with the software on a subsequent occasion. The package will contain the necessary routines to save and load files, which you invoke either by typing a command or selecting a menu option.

4 Although most packages will organize the data, text, or image files in their own special way, many will allow you to save the files, if you wish, in a standard form, such as ASCII in the case of text, and to load files that have been so saved. This means that files created on one package can be *imported* into another, with certain limitations (such as loss of emboldening and other enhancements in the case of text files).

5 When using a software package, you may want to print your work. Most packages will allow you to use a range of different printers, and will adapt the output for your particular model. All you have to do is select your printer from the list that is supported by the software.

Activity

Practise using examples of simple application software such as those contained in the notepad and calendar in Microsoft's Windows, or painting software such as that supplied with GEM (or Windows). If possible, use the software to carry out a realistic and useful job, such as producing your own *to do* list, or a drawing needed for an assignment. Use a range of the facilities provided by the software, and carry out tasks such as saving your work, retrieving it, and printing it.

Assignment 4

In Assignment 2, you selected a computer which you felt was suitable for your work as camp organizer. In Assignment 3, you listed the tasks that you would carry out on this computer. Drawing on the conclusions reached in those assignments, carry out the following tasks.

a Investigate some of the office administration software that is available for your selected computer, and choose suitable packages for the tasks in your list. For help, refer to software reviews in magazines and other sources, as well as sales literature.

b Draft a report on the software packages you have chosen, including a brief account of their main facilities. You should give the reasons for your choice of software, and explain how it will assist in the tasks you identified in Assignment 2.

c Produce the final version of your report using a word processing package, and hand the print-out to your tutor.

Recap

● *Software* is the program of instructions that enables the computer to perform the tasks that we require. It consists of *system software*, to perform the various computer housekeeping tasks, and *application software*, to perform record keeping, word processing, and other computer applications.

- Software instructions operate on the CPU by opening and closing switches in circuits, so controlling the flow of data.

- The CPU understands instructions in *machine code*, i.e. strings of binary 0s and 1s. These are difficult for human programmers to understand and write, and so *high-level programming languages* have been developed to speed up programming. In these, instructions are written using English-like commands. Special software called *interpreters* and *compilers* convert these to the machine code that the computer understands.

- Large computer projects are very expensive and subject to extensive overruns, largely because of bugs. Software engineering practice attempts to remove the inherent unreliability of software by adopting formal methods of program specification, which allow mathematical verification prior to coding, and the use of modern non-procedural programming languages, such as object-oriented programming languages.

- System software consists of *operating systems*, *operating environments*, and *utilities*. Operating systems enable you to perform a comprehensive range of computer housekeeping, but they are normally awkward to use as you have to learn their command structure. Operating environments are less flexible, but they are generally user-friendly, i.e. they are easy to use, and present you with a natural graphics-orientated display. Also, they can make excellent use of the mouse, so minimizing the amount of keyboarding that has to be done. Utilities extend the power of the operating system, as well as allowing you to perform operating system tasks more easily.

- Each file stored on a computer disk is given a name, which is often split into two parts: the *stem* and the *extension*. Often, the extension indicates the type of file that it is, whether a document, a spreadsheet file, or a program file.

- Hard disks can hold many thousands of files, so they need to be organized in *directories*. As a general rule, each software package on a hard disk will be stored in its own directory. Directories form a *tree structure*, with several levels of subdirectories, all within the *root directory* of the disk.

- There are, today, many thousands of application software packages available for microcomputers, especially the PC. They include *communications software, record-keeping software, word processing software, spreadsheets, business graphics, expert systems, computer-aided design, music, painting and animation.*

Answers to questions

1 The computer housekeeping tasks you would need to perform include formatting disks, copying files, deleting files, and organizing files on your disks, especially your hard disk. The applications you might wish to use your computer for include:

- keeping track of income and expenditure and producing the camp accounts
- recording bookings and producing receipts for deposits and final payments
- sending letters, confirmation of bookings, reminder slips, or other documentation to participants
- producing drawings and leaflets to promote the camp and for camp activities
- organizing ideas and plans, and producing a diary of events.

2 *Multi-tasking* means the ability to run several tasks at the same time. Most office users have to carry out several kinds of jobs – such as writing memos or letters, looking up names and addresses or other data in a database, or carrying out calculations on a spreadsheet– and it is very convenient to be able to switch directly from one to another at the press of a key. As well as this, two or three tasks can appear in windows on the screen at the same time, so that you can copy data from one task to another. Another advantage is that tasks that take a great deal of time – such as printing a long document – can take place in the background while you are working at another task on the computer.

5: Technical convergence

Objectives

After reading this chapter, you should be able to:
- outline the characteristics of analogue and digital systems, and the differences between them
- describe how information in analogue form can be converted to digital form and vice versa
- explain the principles underlying the storage, processing, and reproduction of audio and video materials
- describe the main types of storage media, including magnetic tape, compact disc, and video disc
- explain the relevance of this technology to other aspects of IT, and describe the possibilities that arise from linking audio and video equipment to the computer, including interactive video.

Scenario

As youth club leader, you may want to make use of audio and video equipment, including audio and video recorders, and you may wish to link this equipment to computers. Commercially produced audio and video programmes abound, and you may wish to produce your own.

Technological convergence

One of the key features of the information revolution is the *convergence* of the various technologies for handling information, such as computing, audio, video, and telecommunications. I mean by this that computer systems, audio systems, video systems, telecommunications systems, and so on, can be linked together so that the same information can be handled and processed by them all.

Another term used to express a similar idea is *multimedia*, i.e. the bringing together of the various media technologies and harnessing them to the power of the computer. Virtual reality systems, compact disc interactive systems, and other new and exciting products are the direct result of work in this area, and these are described later in this chapter.

Here are a few examples of technological convergence:

● pictures from a video camera or scanner can be fed into a computer, processed in various ways, transmitted down the telephone line, and printed as part of a document

● some computer systems are able to access data, audio, and video stored on compact disc, so that products like encyclopedias, recorded on compact disc, are amenable to sophisticated and rapid computer retrieval techniques, as well as providing sound and pictures

● some video recorders incorporate computer chips and RAM, so that, for example, a video image can be digitized (see below), stored as computer data, and displayed as a high-quality still-frame image or input to a computer system for further processing

● cameras are available that record snapshots on magnetic disk or RAM, for later viewing via a TV, or processing and publishing via a computer system

● increasingly, computers of different organizations are being linked directly over the telephone line using a technology called *electronic data interchange* (EDI), so that ordering and invoicing can be done entirely electronically rather then by sending paper documents through the post.

The possibilities raised by audio, video, and computer convergence are explored in this chapter. The convergence of telecommunications and computing is covered in the next chapter.

Question

1 Jot down two ways in which you might take advantage of these possibilities in your role as youth club leader.

Analogue and digital information

Computers deal with information in digital form, i.e. as sequences of binary 0s and 1s. Human beings, in contrast, handle audio and visual information in analogue form, i.e. as sound waves and light waves. Audio and video systems also handle information mainly in analogue form. Technological convergence therefore demands that devices are available which can convert information between these two forms.

In this section you will learn how information is encoded in analogue form, the principles behind its conversion to digital form, and the devices that are used for this. You will also learn why the analogue world of audio and video is benefiting from the introduction of digital devices such as compact discs.

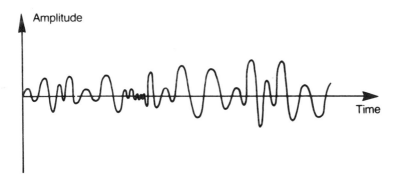

Figure 5.1 An analogue signal

Analogue information

Figure 5.1 shows the possible wave structure of an analogue signal, such as that produced by a sound source. The information in the signal is embodied in the *amplitude* and the *wavelength* of the waves at each point along the horizontal axis of the graph.

Here's what we mean by amplitude, wavelength and other terms that are used in connection with this type of signal.

● *Amplitude* is the distance between the base line and the peak of the wave. It gives the loudness of an audio signal, or the brightness of a video signal.

- *Wavelength* is the span of a complete wave cycle, i.e. the horizontal distance from one peak to the next. Longer wavelengths give deeper notes in the case of audio signals and redder colours in the case of video. Shorter wavelengths give higher notes (audio) or bluer colours (video).

- *Frequency* is the inverse of wavelength. The longer the wavelength, the lower the frequency. Frequency is measured as the number of wave cycles that pass a fixed point in a second. Since sound travels through air at 330 metres per second, we could also measure the frequency of a sound wave using the formula 330/wavelength. The answer will be in cycles per second, or Hertz (Hz); 1,000 cycles per second is 1 kHz, and a million cycles per second is 1 MHz. The lowest note on a piano has a frequency of about 27 Hz; the highest frequency that humans can hear is about 20,000 Hz (20 kHz).

- *Bandwidth* measures the range of frequencies covered by a signal. Human speech covers a range from around 50 Hz to 12 kHz, and so its bandwidth is about 12 kHz. Bandwidth can also mean the range of frequencies that a communications medium such as radio or the telephone can handle – for example, a telephone line has a bandwidth of about 4 kHz.

- *Noise* refers to extraneous signals that interfere with the message signal. In the case of audio messages, noise can be caused by natural background sounds, by hiss on the recording tape, or by hum from faulty components. In the case of video, noise can be caused, for instance, by a bright light source interfering with the picture, or tiny faults in the recording tape. Noise will exist in any system; what is important is that at any frequency its amplitude should be tiny compared to the amplitude of the message, so that it does not act as a distraction or impair the intelligibility of the message.

Digital information

Information in digital form consists of a series of pulses, a pulse representing a binary 1, the absence of a pulse representing a 0.

Although this is quite different from our more familiar analogue world of sound waves and light waves, a number of analogue concepts still apply. In particular, *bandwidth* measures the number of bits that can be transmitted per second over a communications link. In certain circumstances this is called the *baud rate*.

Processing information in digital rather than analogue form offers a number of advantages. One, already mentioned, is the fact that the information can be handled by microprocessors. Another is the fact that information in this form does not normally suffer any *degradation*, i.e. it is reproduced with 100% accuracy.

The reason for this is that a binary 0 does not (normally) change to a 1 through being processed by an electronic device and a 1 does not change to a 0. If an error of this sort does occur, it can normally be picked up and rectified by an automatic error-checking routine. Any low-level noise, which causes slight distortions of the pulses, will be totally ignored by the system. That's why data on a computer disk can be copied and recopied perfectly through any number of generations.

Analogue information, in contrast, does degrade, so that the original signal can *never* be perfectly reproduced. Its wave structure will be slightly corrupted, and some noise will be introduced. Although this degradation will normally be slight, it has a cumulative effect, as is painfully observed when an audio tape is copied and recopied through several generations.

Question

2 You have just bought a compact disc system. The quality of reproduction of your favourite music is (a) much better than you got from your old music centre, but (b) it is not perfect. Explain why this is.

Analogue-to-digital conversion

The conversion of analogue information to digital form, or *digitization*, involves measuring the wave at frequent intervals and converting the results to digits (whole numbers). It's as though the waveform is drawn on a piece of graph paper, and readings from the vertical scale taken for each tiny interval along the horizontal scale, as illustrated in Figure 5.2. These readings, converted to binary form, comprise the digital message.

Once in digital form, the information can be processed and stored with 100% fidelity. However, in the case of audio or video, it is necessary to convert the information back to analogue form when it is finally reproduced from a loudspeaker or TV. You can think of this as

111

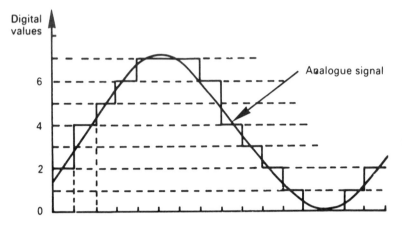

Figure 5.2 Analogue-to-digital conversion

reversing the process shown in Figure 5.2, i.e. drawing a waveform from a series of plotted points. The waveform will now have the stepped appearance shown in the figure, but provided the intervals between each reading are very small (which they are), it will be virtually indistinguishable from the original.

Examples of devices used for analogue-to-digital conversions or vice versa include:

● video digitizers to convert the signal from a video camera to computer input
● scanners to convert an image on paper to computer input
● sound samplers to digitize audio signals
● modems to convert computer output to analogue form for transmission over the phone line, and to convert analogue signals from the phone line to computer input.

Audio and video systems

An information system consists of devices to input, store, process, and output information. Figure 5.3 compares these stages for computer, audio, and video system. I'll deal very briefly with these stages for audio systems, then in rather more detail for video.

	COMPUTER SYSTEM	AUDIO SYSTEM	VIDEO SYSTEM
INPUT	Keyboard or other input device	Microphone	Video camera
PROCESSING	Calculating and editing in CPU	Mixing in sound studio; cutting tape	Mixing in studio; electronic editing of videotape
STORAGE	RAM Magnetic disk Magnetic tape	Magnetic tape	Magnetic tape
OUTPUT	Monitor Printer	Amplifier Loudspeaker	TV set Monitor

Figure 5.3 Three kinds of information processing system

Audio systems

● *Input* — this stage converts sound waves travelling through the air into electrical waves in a wire, using some form of microphone. Common types are carbon microphones, moving-coil (used in telephones), crystal (used on cheap cassette recorders), and, for high-quality work, ribbon and electrostatic.

● *Processing* — once the sound waves have been converted into electrical signals, they can be processed in a number of ways. For example, in a musical recording the amplitude of a certain range of frequencies may be increased, perhaps to emphasize the vocal element of the sound. Another example is mixing the sounds from the number of microphones or other sources using a sound control console.

● *Storage (recording)* – the result of this audio processing is recorded on magnetic tape, which in a professional studio may be the reel-to-reel variety running at 7.5 inches per second.

● *Output (reproduction)* – this stage consists of an amplifier to boost the electrical current generated by the playback head of the tape system, and a loudspeaker.

Question

3 State one way in which you might use a tape-based audio system in your role as youth club leader/summer camp organizer, and list the items of audio equipment you would need for this.

Video systems

Video, like cine film, works by producing an apparently moving picture from a series of still frames. The human eye needs about $\frac{1}{15}$ of a second to register a fresh image, and so frames which change faster than this appear to move. With cine, the frames are projected onto the screen at the rate of 24 per second, whereas with video the rate is 25 per second. These rates are appreciably faster than can be detected by the eye.

However, although the individual frames cannot be distinguished at this speed, there is still a noticeable flicker as each frame flashes on or off. To overcome this the display rate is doubled, to show each frame twice for $\frac{1}{50}$ of a second. In cine this is achieved by a shutter inside the projector which shoots across the frame while it is being displayed. In video this is achieved by a technique known as *interlacing*, described later.

The input device for video is, of course, the video camera. I'll outline first how a monochrome camera works, and then explain how colour is achieved.

Light from a scene is focused by the lens on a target plate inside the casing (see Figure 5.4). This plate is coated with a chemical that emits electrons when light strikes it, the number of electrons varying with the brightness. Loss of electrons from a spot on the plate creates a positive charge at that spot, the strength of the charge corresponding to the number of electrons that have been given off. So areas of light and dark on the scene generate areas of varying positive electrical charges on the plate.

Each spot on the plate is scanned by a beam of electrons emitted by a cathode at the back of the camera. A spot with a high positive charge will absorb many electrons, one with a low charge will absorb few. The electrons which are not absorbed pass through the target plate and are picked up by a signal plate just behind the lens

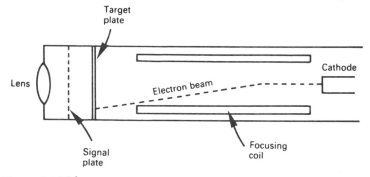

Figure 5.4 Video camera

(see Figure 5.4). Here, they generate an electrical current with an intensity corresponding to that of the beam, and therefore to the charge of the spot on the target plate.

The electron beam itself is very narrow, and it is deflected across the surface of the target plate by a magnetic field generated by an electrical coil in the tube. This field forces the beam to scan each spot on the plate in turn, starting at the top left and moving across the plate in horizontal lines. The entire plate is scanned in this way in a fraction of a second.

In the PAL system, used through most of Western Europe, the Middle East, Africa, South America, and Australasia, 625 scanning lines are used. Similar to PAL is the SECAM system used in France and Eastern Europe and the former Soviet Union. In the NTSC system, used in North America, Japan, and the Philippines, there are only 525 lines, which gives a poorer picture resolution. High-definition TV systems are currently under development which will give much better picture resolutions.

When the picture is finally reproduced on a monitor or TV the same number of scanning lines have to be used, and the electrical current that encodes the picture signal has to be synchronized with the scanning process, so that each spot on the target plate is reproduced in the correct location on the screen. This synchronization is achieved by what's called the *line sync pulse*, which is recorded with the video signal.

I mentioned earlier that each video frame or picture has to be scanned twice in order to avoid flicker. In both the camera and the monitor this is achieved by *interlacing*, i.e. by scanning in two

115

passes. The first pass scans in the even-numbered lines, the second pass scans the odd numbers.

The rate at which each pass is run is determined by the mains frequency. In countries with the PAL and SECAM systems, mains frequency is 50 Hz, so there are 50 passes per second, and therefore 25 frames (since each frame requires two passes). In countries with the NTSC system, mains frequency is 60 Hz, giving 60 passes and therefore 30 frames a second.

To achieve a colour video picture the camera has to have three tubes, each containing a cathode ray gun to emit electrons. The light entering the lens is split into its red, green, and blue primary colours by a system of mirrors, and each colour is processed by a different tube to give three electrical currents leaving the camera. These, ultimately, are fed to three colour guns inside the monitor or TV tube when the picture is reproduced.

The video output device – i.e. the TV set or monitor – is rather like a video camera in reverse. The red, green, and blue signals are fed to the three electron guns, which shoot narrow beams of electrons at the screen. These are deflected by magnets, which force them to scan the screen to reproduce the 625 scanning lines.

The front of the tube is coated on the inside with tiny spots of a chemical which glows red, green, or blue, or a combination of these colours (to make other hues), depending on which guns are firing at it. Each spot is, in fact, made up of three separate dots, one for each of the three colours. The intensity of the colour produced by a dot depends on the intensity of the electron beam at that moment, which in turn depends upon the amplitude of the signal feeding the gun.

Like audio, video is recorded on magnetic tape. However, video recording technology is more complex, owing to the very large amount of information contained in a video picture that has to be laid down on the tape. The bandwidth for video is in fact 5.5 MHz, compared to 20 kHz for audio.

The technique used to squeeze all this information on the tape involves laying down the recording in parallel tracks across its width instead of along its length (see Figure 5.5). The recorded tracks are very densely packed, so allowing a one-centimetre length of tape to hold up to two or three metres of recorded signal.

The most common recording process is *helical scanning*. In this, two recording heads, mounted on opposite sides of a tilted rotating

Videotape

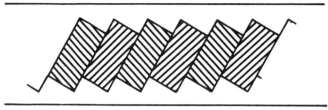

Figure 5.5 Pattern of tracks on a video recording

drum, fly across the tape and set up the pattern of tracks shown in the figure. The speed of rotation is 25 revolutions per second in the PAL system, and 30 rps in NTSC systems, so in one revolution each head lays down a track scanning one field of a video frame, the two tracks together giving one complete interlaced frame.

The audio part of the signal is recorded along the length of the video tape, at one edge, and the field sync pulse controlling the running of the tape is recorded along the other edge. These tracks are recorded and played back by a separate system of heads, and any attempt to edit the tape by cutting completely upsets the playback at that point. Video editing is therefore a process that involves copying the required sequences onto a new tape rather than (as with film) cutting and splicing existing tape.

Activity

Turn to the end of this chapter and read the assignment work you will be doing. In preparation for this, make a list of the equipment you will require. Then visit your college's audio-visual centre to see their range of equipment, and book time to use the resources you need for your assignment.

Technological convergence in audio systems

The power of the computer is increasingly being harnessed to enhance the potential of audio systems. Here are some examples.

● *Electronic keyboards* are microprocessor-based devices which can generate electronically a wide repertoire of sounds and other effects which in the past could only be achieved by traditional musical instruments. They can also generate automatically a range of accompaniments to a tune.

● Many musical instruments which produce an electrical output, such as electronic keyboards, can be linked directly to other electronic equipment such as computers by means of a *midi* interface. The processing power of the computer can then be brought to bear on a musical composition, to produce effects which cannot be economically produced by other means. For example, the notes from a single instrument can be processed to produce the effect of an entire orchestra.

● The playback of an audio programme can be controlled by computer using a technique known as *interactive audio*. The most popular application of this is in language learning, in which the learner listens to an audio sequence and then answers some questions on the computer screen. The computer grades the learner's responses, and then, depending on his or her performance, fast winds the tape to another sequence or repeats the same sequence. The technique is similar in principle to that used in interactive video, described later in this chapter.

Technological convergence in video systems

The power of the computer can greatly enhance the capabilities of video systems. Here are some examples.

● Some modern video recorders are able to store video pictures in semiconductor memory, to produce a variety of effects such as high-quality still frames, multi-image displays, or picture-in-picture effects. Colours can be changed, and patterns and other electronic effects can be created on the screen. These effects may not be of much use in the home, but are of value in clubs and other settings.

● The computer is being increasingly used to generate special video effects and animation, using sophisticated computer graphics software and animation software. For example, it is no longer necessary to produce by hand every frame of an animated cartoon. Nowadays, the artist need only to produce the key frames, and the computer will generate the intermediate ones.

- Video images, when digitized, can be fed into a computer system, where they can be manipulated in a variety of ways, or used as a source of images for desktop publishing applications.
- The playback of a video programme can be controlled by computer, using a technique known as *interactive video*, or IV. This is now widely used in computer-based training, especially in the United States. IV is described later in this chapter.

Activity

If possible, explore the possibilities offered by technological convergence for yourself, using whatever systems are available in your college. These might include a video camera connected via a digitizer to a computer system, or a microcomputer which can interface with a musical keyboard, or an interactive video system.

Multimedia

Multimedia refers to the convergence of audio, video, and other technologies with computer technology. This convergence is facilitated by the trend towards the digitization of all forms of information, including digital audio systems, digital TV, and so on. By harnessing the computer to these various media technologies, powerful training, entertainment, and presentation systems can be created. They are described in the remaining sections of this chapter.

Multimedia applications often involve the use of the computer to control equipment such as videodisc players, and mixing the video images with the computer's own output. It also includes the use of the PC with equipment such as video cameras and microphones to capture and edit video and audio input. At present, the main multimedia technologies and applications are:

- interactive video, used mainly for training
- computer animation, using software such as Autodesk's Animator, incorporating video and audio material
- the use of data compression techniques to greatly reduce the amount of disk space occupied by video and other images; compression ratios of over 100:1 are possible.

Interactive video

Interactive video systems (IV) allow the user to control a video programme using a computer. In practice, this means that the computer and video output appear together on the screen, the computer output often taking the form of either questions on the video sequence just seen or a menu of choices for further sequences. The viewer makes his or her response by typing at the keyboard, and the computer acts on this to determine which sequences of the video programme are played next.

IV can be achieved by linking a modified home video recorder to a computer. However, videodisc is a much better medium, for reasons which are explained in the next section.

The main application of IV is in education and training. The videodisc in this case will normally consist of many short sequences, each one lasting just a few minutes. The video is controlled by computer software in the form of a training package written using special programming language called an authoring language. This software carries out the following tasks:

- It controls the order in which the video sequences are to be played. This can be modified by the learner, either by selecting menu choices or through the way in which he or she responds to questions. A learner with difficulties may be routed by the program through different sequences to a learner who answers the questions correctly.
- It displays questions on the screen to test the learner's understanding of the video sequence just seen.
- It matches the learner's response to a question against a number of possible responses that are stored in the program, and so marks it right or wrong.
- It provides feedback to the user, encouraging him or her in the case of correct answers and giving explanations in the case of incorrect answers.
- It keeps track of the learner's score for assessment purposes, and of the parts of the course that he or she found difficult.

IV has been found to be a very effective training tool. It has the following advantages over conventional training methods:

- because the video sequences are interspersed with computer question-and-answer sequences, the learner has to apply his or her learning at frequent and regular intervals, which helps retention and understanding of the material

● the computer gives immediate feedback when the learner has typed an answer, and provides remedial instruction in the case of wrong answers; this is highly motivating, as well as ensuring that the learner has understood each point

● the learner's route through the material can be geared to his or her needs

● because an impersonal machine rather than a human tutor is assessing work, the learner is less embarrassed and demotivated by wrong answers

● the material can be presented in a form which is visually attractive and stimulating.

Another major application of IV is point-of-sale (POS). Customers are able to quickly access video sequences on the products that interest them, or find out more about the services offered by a bank or other institution. IV has been successfully used in DSS offices, where it allows clients to determine their rights and benefits without needing to speak with an official.

Videodisc

IV can be based upon videotape or videodisc. The former is relatively low-cost, and can incorporate video material produced fairly cheaply by the training institution itself. However, it has a number of disadvantages compared to the more sophisticated videodisc system described below:

● it takes a long time to wind through the tape to the start of a video sequence, unless that sequence is very close to the previous one

● it cannot pinpoint sequences in the precise way that is possible with videodisc

● it cannot pause on a video frame without distorting the image on the screen and, ultimately, wearing out the tape at that point

● programming the computer-based material for videotape is time-consuming, owing to the slow search time and the lack of an accurate frame numbering system.

For these reasons, videodisc material is much more suitable for IV. The two main videodisc systems are Laservision (developed by

Philips) and JVC's VHD system (which is based on electrical capacitance rather than on the optical technology described below). Both types of disc are 30 cm across, the same size as long-play music records.

Laservision discs store information in the form of tiny pits burned by laser light in the disk's surface. Unlike compact discs laservision discs work on analogue rather than digital principles: the pits are in fact 'slices' of the waves recorded on them, as shown in Figure 5.6. Both the width of the pits and angles of the edges

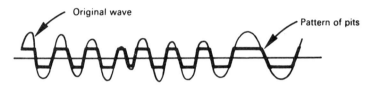

Figure 5.9 Clipped waveform pattern of pits on a Laservision disc

vary, and on playback these variations are measured by a narrow laser beam which is reflected from them onto the reading head of the laservision player. There is no physical contact between the surface of the disc and the reading head, so Laservision discs are not worn out by repeated playings.

Laservision discs for interactive video are called *active play* discs. Each circular track of an active play disc stores one complete video frame (picture). The player rotates the disc at a constant angular velocity of 25 revolutions per second to play back the video at the standard speed of 25 frames per second.

If you think about this, you will realize that, unlike an ordinary music record, the player must spin the disc faster when it is reading the outer tracks of the disc than when it is reading the inner tracks. This makes for a complex playback mechanism, but it provides the user with a very versatile system:

● If the reading head is held stationary over one rotating track, one frame is reproduced and held on the screen. The reproduction is perfect, unlike the awful picture you get when you try to hold a videotape on a single frame. This means that you can use a videodisc to store still pictures, such as sets of slides. An active-play disc can store 36 minutes of video per side, and since each second of video playback uses 25 frames, it is easy to work out the number of still pictures that can be stored on one side of a disc:

$$36 \times 60 \times 25 = 54\,000 \text{ pictures.}$$

● Each frame can be identified by a number, and the player can access any frame simply by moving the reading head to the corresponding track. Any frame from the 54 000 stored on a side of a disc can be accessed in under 2 seconds. It is this numbering system that is used by the associated computer software to control the videoplayer.

To make a videodisc, the video sequences must first be shot using the professional C-format video system. When the final tape is edited and ready, a videodisc master is produced from it using a laser light process, and the individual discs are pressed from this.

The production of the video film is the most expensive part of the process, though other elements, such as writing the associated computer program, are not cheap. The total cost of producing an interactive videodisc, with the software, is likely to exceed £100 000. As a result, IV training packages are expensive, often several hundred pounds per copy – which is why there are not too many of them around in colleges. Nevertheless, IV packages are widely used in a number of big companies, where the large numbers who use them make this powerful training medium a cost-effective tool.

Compact discs

Compact discs are now widely used for music recordings. As explained in Chapter 3, compact discs store information in a digital form, which means that, unlike ordinary analogue recordings, there is no degradation of the signal. If the reproduction is less than perfect, then the fault lies with the other analogue parts of the system – such as the microphones and the loudspeakers – rather than the compact discs themselves.

Being digital, compact discs clearly have an important role in the digital world of IT. For besides audio recordings, they can be used to store computer data and text, as well as video images in digital form. Interactive video systems based upon compact disc are likely to be much more significant in the future then IV systems based on videodisc.

Laser light represents a binary 1 by a short pulse of light from a laser gun, and a binary 0 by the absence of a pulse. To record information on a compact disc, very powerful pulses of laser light are used, which burn tiny pits in its surface. As the disc rotates, and the laser gun works its way like a gramophone stylus across the surface, a tightly-packed spiral of tracks consisting of thousands of tiny pits is built up.

On playback, the process works in reverse. A low-powered laser beam scans the tracks of the rotating disc, being reflected back by the silvered surface. The pits on the surface are one quarter of the wavelength of the laser light in depth, so light reflected from the bottom of a pit is exactly out of phase with light reflected from the surface. It therefore interferes with it, largely cancelling it out. The returning beam strikes a photoelectric cell, which converts the light to electrical pulses. The less intense light from a pit produces a smaller pulse than light reflected from a spot on the surface which doesn't contain a pit. In this way the original pattern of 1s and 0s is reproduced (see Figure 5.7).

As with videodisc, there is no physical contact between the surface of the disc and the playback mechanism, and so no wear is

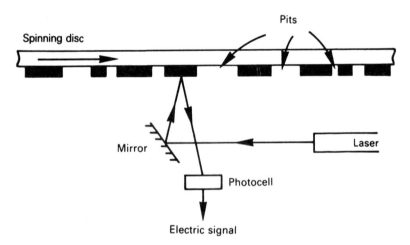

Figure 5.8 Compact disc scanning system

caused by repeated playings, and grease or dust normally has no effect. Unlike videodisc, a compact disc is only 5.25 inches across, the same as an ordinary floppy disk.

Compact disc for multimedia applications

The huge capacity of compact discs means that they can store large amounts of computer data, text, images, and sound. Encyclopedias, for example, are now being published in compact disc form. This not only reduces their physical size, it also means that, since they can be linked to the power of the computer, all entries on a selected topic can be rapidly retrieved and displayed on the screen.

Another development is *CD-V*, short for 'Compact Disc – Video', which will be used for high-quality sound and video. One obvious application for CD-V is pop videos.

There are also interesting possibilities of computer-controlled multimedia presentations using compact disc systems. These could form a low-cost alternative to IV systems. Philips, for example, has been working for a number of years on *CD-I*, which stands for 'Compact Disc – Interactive', and has now, in 1992, brought out a mass-market CD-I player. This costs a fraction of the price of a videodisc player, and uses comparatively inexpensive compact discs. Quite a number of CD-I discs have already been produced, covering topics as diverse as photography, golf, and language learning.

CD-I aims to take full advantage of the enormous capacity of compact discs for storing images and sounds as well as text, and combine this with the power of the computer to develop a new publishing medium. This will revolutionize encyclopedias, dictionaries, training materials, and so on, which ideally contain visual, aural, and textual components. A single disc is able to hold a complete English-language dictionary, including the words in audio and some accompanying pictures in (still) video.

Like interactive video, the computer software allows the user to access any part of the disc by means of a system of menus or questions, and if necessary will conduct him or her through the disc as part of a training package, with questions, feedback, and branching.

Unlike interactive video, the pictures are digitized, and have to be read from the disc and processed by the computer before they can be displayed on the screen. The Philips machine has two video processors, which means that it can display simultaneously two different signals from the disc, e.g. text and real pictures. So it can be used in much the same way as interactive video, at a fraction of the (hardware) price.

Two competing multimedia compact disc systems that have also reached the market are Intel's Digital Video Interactive (DVI) system and Commodore's CDTV (Commodore Dynamic Total Vision). At the moment, Philips CD-I seems to be technically superior, but things change rapidly in the highly competitive world of computing and multimedia.

Data compression

In order to reduce the amount of space occupied by video images, data compression techniques are employed. Intel's DVI chip set, for example, can achieve compression ratios of around 160:1. The speed of compression (to store the image) and decompression (to reproduce the image) are very fast, and we are not far off the day when full-motion high-resolution video can be reproduced by a PC from compressed files.

Data compression uses the fact that a great deal of information in an image or sequence of images is redundant. For example, expanses of sky do not change from pixel to pixel within an individual frame, nor from frame to frame within a sequence of frames. This redundant data can therefore be discarded, all that is needed is the data for a single pixel together with the area of the frame, and the sequence of frames, to which it applies.

A variety of mathematical techniques are used to increase the amount of compression. For example, the Philips CD-I system employs a compression technique called *Discrete Cosine Transform* (DCT), which breaks down each frame into blocks, and compares how these change from frame to frame. If there is little change from frame to frame the blocks can be bigger, and less code is therefore needed to produce a succession of frames.

Virtual reality systems

You have probably seen examples of interactive video material, such as the BBC's *Domesday Project*, perhaps on TV. If so, you will know that many videodiscs include numerous shots of buildings, streets, or towns taken from many angles, and that the computer-driven interactive part of the system allows you to 'travel' around the building or town. Unlike an ordinary film, with this system you can choose which way to go (by perhaps pointing and clicking with the mouse), and you can pause in any location and look around before proceeding.

It's a bit like real life, except that it only impacts your visual senses – you can't, for example, touch any of the objects you are looking at, and you are always aware that you are not really 'there' but are in fact sat in front of a monitor. But what if you could 'touch' the objects, and what if you could see them in three dimensions on a wrap-around screen? And what if you could move around by some more natural means than pushing and clicking a mouse?

Well, systems are around that can do this, and they transport the user into a 'virtual reality' – something that closely simulates real life.

Virtual reality systems were first developed by NASA in the mid-1980s, to solve the problem of repairing space stations. Ideally, it wanted to use robots to work in the hostile environment of space, but there are repair situations where human skills are essential. Its solution was to feed signals from the video camera in the robot's 'head' to the human astronaut on the ground, and relay back to the robot the movements of the astronaut's hands. So a headset was developed containing two tiny TV sets, one for each eye, to give stereo vision. It also contained tracking circuitry to transmit movements of the astronaut's head to the robot, so that the camera automatically pointed wherever the astronaut wished to look. The astronaut also wore a *dataglove* which could transmit the movements of his hands and fingers to the robot.

Today, half a decade later, virtual reality systems have progressed considerably:

● the headset now contains stereo earphones for sound
● the user may sit in a console of some kind which simulates the movement of aircraft or other transportation
● in many virtual reality applications, the whole system is hooked up to a computer, which generates the simulated environment. In these systems the dataglove will be programmed to interpret

certain movements as commands; for example, if you wish to move through the simulated enviroment, you simply point your finger in the desired direction
- instead of a dataglove it is now possible to don an entire 'datasuit' so that movements of the entire body can be electronically sensed and transmitted.

Virtual reality applications include:

- flight test simulators
- control of robots and other devices in environments that are impossible for humans – space station maintenance has already been mentioned, but future possibilities seem limitless, from microsurgery (by controlling a tiny surgical device inserted in the patient's body) to testing the design of buildings by walking through computer simulations of them
- entertainment and leisure applications, such as computer 'arcade' games.

Assignment 5

EITHER

Produce a 15-minute audio teaching tape describing how to use the word processing or record-keeping software package you used in the last chapter. The idea is that the learner will load the software into the computer, start the audio tape, and then follow the spoken instructions and explanations.

OR

Carry out an assignment task of your choice which illustrates the potential of technological convergence, such as:
- producing a musical composition using a computer linked to e.g. an electronic keyboard, or
- producing a short interactive video program based on an existing videodisc, using a videodisc player linked to a computer.

THEN

For whichever of the above tasks you carried out, describe briefly the equipment you need for your assignment, outlining the technology used in inputting, storing, processing and outputting the information.

Recap

- A key feature of the information revolution is *technological convergence*, i.e. the linking together of different technologies such as audio, video, and computing so that the same information can be processed by them all. This has led to a wealth of powerful techniques, including digitized images for desktop publishing, computer-generated animations and music, and interactive video.
- Convergence requires the conversion of information between analogue and digital forms using devices such as video digitizers and scanners.
- Audio information is embodied in (analogue) sound waves, video information in (analogue) light waves. The *amplitude* of the wave at any point gives its loudness or intensity, the *wavelength* gives its pitch (in the case of audio) or colour (in the case of video).
- Other terms used in connection with analogue signals include *frequency*, which is the inverse of the wavelength, *bandwidth*, which measures the range of frequencies covered by the signal, and *noise*, which refers to extraneous signals that interfere with the message signal.
- The term bandwidth is also used in connection with digital signals, where it refers to the number of bits per second that can be transmitted over a communications link.
- Processing information in digital rather than analogue form can bring a number of advantages. One is the fact that it can be handled by microprocessors, a second is the fact that the information is not degraded when it is stored or processed.
- Audio and video systems, like computer systems, consist of input, storage, processing, and output stages. In the case of an audio system, input is by *microphone*, storage is on *magnetic tape*, processing is by means of a *sound console* and by *tape editing*, and output is by *loudspeaker*. In the case of a video system, input is by *video camera*, storage is on *magnetic tape*, processing is carried out in a *video studio*, and output is by *monitor* or *TV set*.
- *Compact discs* form an optical recording medium which offers significant advantages over conventional media. They can store up to 600 Mbytes of data, in the form of audio signals, video signals, computer data, or a combination of these. The information is recorded in digital form, as tiny pits on the disc's surface which are detected by a laser light beam. A pit indicates a binary 1, the absence of a pit indicates a binary 0.
- *Videodiscs* are another optical medium used mainly for video recordings. In the case of active play discs, each revolution of the disc generates a single video frame. Any frame can be located in under 2

129

seconds, and high-quality still frames are possible, as well as other effects, such as reverse play.
● When a videodisc player is connected to a computer using suitable interfacing equipment and software, *interactive video* is possible. This example of technological convergence is a powerful training medium, allowing the learner to control his route through the video material, and providing a sophisticated testing and feedback capability.
● CD-I, short for *compact disc interactive*, is another example of technological convergence. In this, the compact disc stores audio, video, and computer information, and the system allows a degree of animation. This technology offers some of the potential of interactive video combined with audio compact disc and computer compact disc capabilities, but at a fraction of the price of interactive video.

Answers to questions

1 One use would be to transfer a picture from a video camera into a computer system for printing in a newsletter or magazine. Another would be to link a computer with a video recorder to produce some form of interactive programme, such as is described towards the end of this chapter.

2 (a) Compact discs are a digital recording medium, and so they will store and reproduce audio signals with much greater fidelity than ordinary (analogue) records.
(b) Parts of the system are still analogue, including the amplifier, the microphone that recorded the original music, and the loudspeaker that reproduces it, and this introduces some degradation.

3 One use might be to record your own music group. For this, you might need the following equipment:
● two or three high-quality microphones, probably electrostatic, together with microphone stands
● some form of mixer, possibly a sound control console
● one or more high-quality loudspeakers to check the balance and quality of the output
● reel-to-reel tape recorder to produce the master tape
● a cassette recorder if audio cassettes are to be produced from the master.

6: Communications

Objectives

After reading this chapter, you should be able to:
- outline the principles of analogue and digital communications
- explain the importance of technological convergence for communications
- describe the main types of communications systems, including computer-to-computer communications, computer networks, telephone networks, and broadcast networks
- describe a range of telecommunications services, such as facsimile, electronic mail, and on-line databases.

Scenario

In your role as youth club leader, you may want to set up communications links between your computer and other equipment, including other computers, in order to pass information between them. Some of this equipment – such as a printer – may be in your own office; some, however, may be situated in remote locations, and may include computers offering a range of services over the telephone network, such as on-line databases and electronic mail.

You may also wish to use other types of communications equipment, including the telephone, telex, and facsimile.

What do we mean by communications?

In the context of IT, *communications* refers to the transfer of messages in the form of electromagnetic signals, and ranges from satellite

131

broadcasts and computer-to-computer communications, to the ordinary telephone. These signals can take the form of:

● radio waves travelling through the air or through space
● electrical currents flowing along a wire
● pulses of laser light travelling along optic fibres.

Some electromagnetic communications take place over very short distances, for example the communications that take place between your computer and its printer when you select the print option in an application package. We shall refer to these as *local communications*. Many electromagnetic communications, however, take place over a distance, and these are referred to as *telecommunications*.

Telecommunications can be split into two major divisions:

● *radio and TV*, which are mainly intended for audio and video broadcasts, but which nowadays are also used for communicating computer data, e.g. by satellite link
● *telephone networks*, originally designed for voice, but now also used to send

    – computer data, using e.g. British Telecom's Datel services
    – text, using e.g. telex
    – image, using e.g. facsimile

These telecommunications services, and others, are described later in this chapter.

Question

1 List the ways in which local communications and telecommunications might prove useful to you in your role as youth club leader. Your list might contain up to ten or more entries– to start you off, here are two:
● contacting members over the phone
● looking up information on local events using an on-line database such as Prestel.

How do electromagnetic communications work?

The communications process involves three stages:

1 the conversion of information, i.e. data, text, image, or voice, to electromagnetic signals
2 the transmission of these signals to a receiving device
3 the conversion of the signals back to information (data, text, image, or voice).

The equipment used for these three stages for each type of communications is as follows.

Local communications

All that is needed in this case is suitable cabling connecting up the computers and other equipment that are to communicate, and communications software to pass files between them.

Radio and TV broadcasts

Special equipment is needed in this case for each of the three processes listed above:

● microphones and cameras in a studio to convert voice and image to electrical signals
● transmitters to broadcast these signals in the form of radio waves
● radio and TV receivers to pick up these radio waves and convert them back to voice and image.

Telephone communications

This is the most complex of the three forms of communication, in that special equipment is needed not only for the three processes listed above but also to switch or route calls from one subscriber to another. The equipment for long-distance telephony is shown in Figure 6.1 and consists of:

● a microphone in the telephone handset to convert voice to electrical signals, which are sent down a wire to the local telephone exchange
● switching circuits at the exchange to route the call
● a long-distance line or radio links to carry the call to its destination
● switching circuits at the destination exchange to route the call to the receiving handset.

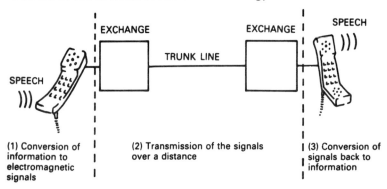

Figure 6.1 Telephone network

Technological convergence and communications

I dealt with technological convergence in the last chapter. In the case of communications, this term refers to the marriage of communications systems with computing and other technologies, a process which today is well advanced, and which is resulting in the digitization of telephone and other telecommunications networks. (Local communications between computers and other computer-based equipment have always been digital.)

Being designed for voice communications, the telephone has always – till now – been an analogue device, converting sound waves impinging on the microphone in the telephone handset to electrical waves travelling down the telephone wire. At the receiving handset, these are converted by the earpiece back to sound waves. However, with advancing technology, this system has become outdated.

For example, there is an increasing volume of computer communications, which require that computer output is first converted to analogue form for transmission over the telephone network, and then back to digital form for input to the destination computer. To handle this conversion, a device called a *modem* must be inserted between the computer's RS232/V24 communications port and the telephone socket. How this device works is explained later.

Also, parts of today's telephone networks now use digital devices. For example, optic fibres using laser light pulses to carry the information in digital form are increasingly being used for long-distance communications (see later).

Technological convergence, and the advantages that follow from it,

134

is causing the public telecommunications authorities in the UK and other advanced countries to convert their telephone networks from analogue to digital systems. This has a number of important implications:

● It means that data communications will no longer require digital-to-analogue conversion. Instead, voice will be digitized for transmission by the network, using a device in the handset called a *codec* (short for *coder/decoder*).

● Message routeing can be controlled by computer, using a technique described later on called *packet switching*. In this, each *packet* of data carries the *address* of the receiving machine, so enabling the network to route it to its destination. This means that a number of messages can share the same lines, in contrast to traditional *circuit switching*, which dedicate lines to individual calls.

● All information – voice, image, text, and data – is sent in a common digital form, i.e. as sequences of pulses, representing binary 0s and 1s. So all types of transmission, whether phone, video, or computer data, can therefore share the same system and equipment. *Integrated services digital network* (ISDN) is the name given to this new type of system.

● The information can be handled by computer, and so a number of facilities can be introduced which would not be practical otherwise. British Telecom's digital service offers over 50 new facilities that were not previously available. (Some of these are described later in this chapter.)

Besides the digitization of telephone networks, digital radio and TV are on the horizon.

Activity

If you have a modem and suitable communications software available, connect the modem to a computer, dial up Prestel, and explore parts of the Prestel database. For example, look up details of higher education courses that you might be interested in taking on completion of your current course.

If you are not a Prestel subscriber, local Prestel phone numbers can be obtained from Telecom, and you can access sample Prestel frames by keying in the identity number 4444444444 and the password 4444.

Fibre optics

Digital communications, using laser light pulses travelling along thin optic fibres, are much more efficient than wire communications, for they allow a very broad bandwidth. This means that they can carry a large number of telephone calls simultaneously, as well as video signals and high-volume computer communications.

So to cope with the ever-increasing volume of data communications of all types, British Telecom is laying optic fibres across the country to link exchanges. These are strands of glass, about 0.1 mm thick, with walls able to reflect the laser pulses and so prevent them escaping. This not only minimizes dissipation of the signal, it also allows it to travel round any bends in the fibre.

During manufacture, individual fibres are laid around a central steel supporting wire and then enclosed within a protective sheath. The resulting cable is physically tough.

Question

2 What three advantages do you think optic fibre cables have for data communications?

The telecommunications problem

The digitization of telecommunications networks alleviates three fundamental problems associated with the transmission of electromagnetic signals over a distance. These are dissipation of the signal, noise, and limited bandwidth.

Dissipation

An electromagnetic signal dissipates (loses its strength) as it travels away from its source, and so it needs periodic boosting. Ways of achieving this are described in this chapter; they include the use of satellites in the case of radio waves, and, in the case of telephone, repeaters located at intervals along trunk lines. Laser signals travelling along optic fibres are not dissipated to the same extent as electrical signals travelling along wires.

Noise

The second problem concerns noise. The signal can be corrupted by, say, electromagnetic noise, i.e. interference from other sources. In the case of telephone, one way of overcoming this is by the use of twisted wire-pairs. The original signal is sent down one wire of the pair, and its mirror image, i.e. an identical out-of-phase signal, is sent down the other. Because the wires are tightly twisted round each other, any electrical interference affects both equally. Figure 6.2 illustrates this – it shows digital pulses travelling down the wires, as well as an interfering wave-like noise. At the receiver a special circuit subtracts the second wire's signal from the first's. This removes the interference, and also reinforces the original signal.

Laser pulses travelling along optic fibres are not affected by this type of interference.

Bandwidth

The third problem concerns bandwidth. Cost considerations limit the bandwidth of a telecommunications circuit, and hence the amount of information that can be transmitted in a given time. In addition, the traditional circuit-switched telephone exchanges, which dedicate a line to a call for the duration of the call, do not make efficient use of the

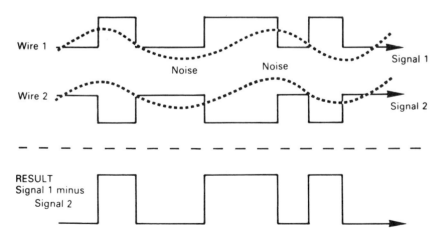

Figure 6.2 Elimination of noise in a twisted-wire pair

available capacity of the line. Modern packet switching, based upon digital communications equipment, allows a number of calls to share the same line. In addition, optic fibres allow broadband communications (i.e. signals with a very broad bandwidth), and so can carry a very large number of simultaneous telephone calls, as well as TV signals.

Carrier waves and modulation

Most radio and telephone communications are based on the analogue microphone/loudspeaker technology outlined in Chapter 5, and it is therefore important that you understand the principles behind this.

Sound waves are converted to electrical waves, which are transmitted over a distance and then converted back to sound. In the case of radio, the electrical waves are amplified and fed to the transmitting aerial, which radiates radio waves of corresponding frequencies. At the receiver, this process is reversed: the radio waves, as they pass by, set up minute electrical currents of the same frequency in the aerial, which are amplified by the receiver.

Like light, radio waves travel in straight lines, which means they cannot bend round the earth's surface. For long-distance transmissions, however, they can be bounced off the *ionosphere*, an ionized layer in the upper atmosphere which reflects radio waves, and then bounced up again from the earth's surface (which is also reflective). Powerful transmissions, bounced repeatedly in this way, can be sent right around the earth.

The power of a radio or telephone signal dissipates as it travels away from its source, and so it may require boosting at intervals on its journey. So the BBC has transmitters in Cyprus and other parts of the world which pick up and re-transmit its external service broadcasts, and telephone companies such as British Telecom use repeaters, installed at intervals on trunk lines, to amplify the signals.

Satellites are also quite widely used, for they are able both to amplify radio signals and overcome the problem of the earth's curvature. A single communications satellite can usually handle a couple of TV channels as well as several thousand telephone conversations.

(The reason why the number of TV channels is limited is the large amount of information that they must carry compared to the amount of information in a telephone call. You will recall from Chapter 5 that this means that a TV channel must have a much broader bandwidth than a telephone channel, i.e. it must embrace a much wider frequency range. The bandwidth of a telephone channel is around 4 kHz, whereas that of a satellite transmitted TV channel is much more than this (around 30 MHz). A single TV channel therefore replaces up to around seven thousand telephone channels.)

Carrier waves

A key feature of this technology is the use of *carrier* waves. These permit a large number of signals to travel simultaneously through the air or space, or down a wire. The signal generated at the microphone, video camera, or other source is superimposed on a fixed-frequency carrier wave, which is transmitted at the same time as carrier waves of other frequencies carrying other signals. The receiver is tuned to pick up a carrier wave of a particular frequency, and from this wave it extracts the original signal.

The process of superimposing the signal on the carrier wave is called *modulation*. Several modulation methods are possible, including amplitude, frequency, and phase.

Amplitude modulation (AM)

This is shown diagrammatically in Figure 6.3. The frequency of the carrier wave is fixed, but its amplitude is governed by the characteristics of the signal. This type of modulation is used for radio broadcasts in this country on the short, medium, and long waves, and a derivative of the basic form is also used on our telephone system. It has the disadvantage that it can be greatly affected by noise generated by atmospheric static and electrical equipment.

Digital information can also be carried in this way, as is illustrated in Figure 6.4.

Frequency modulation (FM)

This is illustrated in Figure 6.5, which shows how digital information modulates the frequency of a carrier wave. In this case, the amplitude of the carrier wave is fixed, but its frequency varies slightly with variations in the signal. FM is used for very high frequency (VHF) radio broadcasts.

139

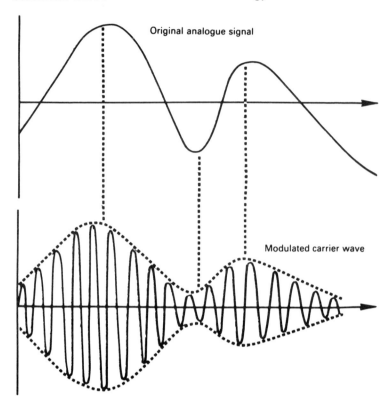

Figure 6.3 Amplitude modulation

Phase modulation (PM)

This can be used to carry digital information, and involves reversing the phase of the carrier wave each time a binary 1 is encountered. The process is also illustrated in Figure 6.5.

Multiplexing

This is the term used to describe techniques which allow a number of different signals to use the same transmission link (normally air space in the case of radio, wire in the case of telephone). The use of carrier waves is one multiplexing technique. Another, suitable for use with digital communications, splits the signals into short *packets*, inter-

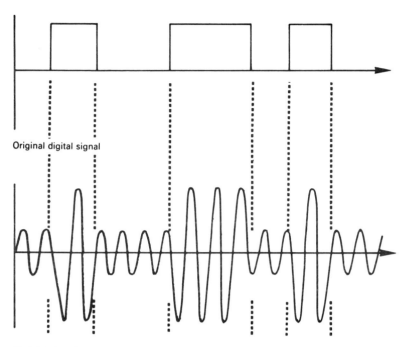

Original digital signal

Modulated carrier wave

Figure 6.4 Amplitude modulation of a digital signal

leaving packets from one signal with those from others. Although each packet is short, it has a broad bandwidth and so carries a relatively large amount of data (see Figure 6.6). At the receiver, the packets are reassembled to form the original message.

Figure 6.6 compares the use of carrier waves and packets as multiplexing methods.

Modems

To transmit digital information from computers over an analogue communications link such as a telephone line it is necessary to use a *modem*. This name is short for *modulator/demodulator*, for the device modulates the outgoing carrier wave with the digital data being transmitted, and demodulates incoming carrier waves to reconstitute the digital signals being received.

141

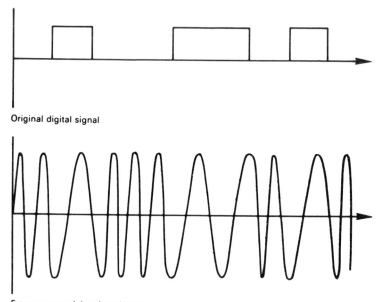

Original digital signal

Frequency-modulated carrier wave

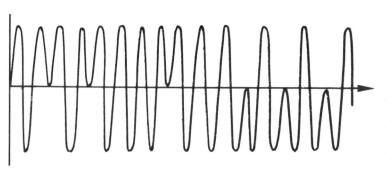

Phase-modulated carrier wave

Figure 6.5 Frequency modulation and phase modulation

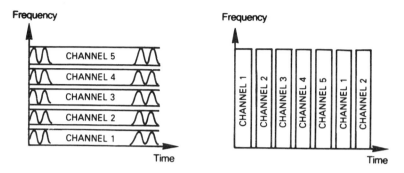

Figure 6.6 Multiplexing technologies

Computer software is also needed to allow the computer to use the modem. This enables you to switch the computer to the correct data transmission and reception settings (see later), as well as ensuring that it displays data received in the correct form. To receive Prestel, for example, you need suitable Prestel software.

Communications systems and networks

This next section deals with the range of communications systems that are available. These include:

- inter-computer communications
- local area networks
- circuit-switched networks
- packet-switched networks
- broadcast networks.

Inter-computer communications

The simplest communications link is a single cable linking two pieces of electronic equipment, the purpose being to transfer data, text, or image files between them. This chapter, written on one type of computer, could be transferred via such a link to a different type of computer, or to electronic typesetting equipment, or to a computer printer.

For this type of communication to work, the data must be transmitted in a form that the receiving equipment can recognize. In other

143

words, there must be communications standards, or *protocols* to which both computers conform. This means that:

1 the baud rate setting of the receiving equipment must be the same as that of the transmitting equipment
2 the way in which the data is organized for communications must be the same for both
3 the code for converting keyboard characters to bits must be the same for both.

With regard to 1, most computers default to a standard send/receive rate of 300 baud, but they can be easily switched to other baud rates. Possible baud rates are 75, 150, 300, 1200, 2400, 4800, 9600, and higher.

For 2, there are standards to which most computers conform, and it is a straightforward matter to switch to other send/receive characteristics. For example, *asynchronous* transmission is normally used, meaning that data is transmitted when it becomes available rather than at fixed intervals (as occurs in *synchronous* transmission). This means that special start and stop bit codes must precede and follow each block of data transmitted, telling the receiver when the data begins and ends. Both computers must adhere to the same bit code standards.

For 3, the ASCII code – short for American Standard Code for Information Interchange – is standard for communications between microcomputers.

Microcomputers typically send and receive data via circuitry which conforms to an internationally agreed standard called RS232. There is a standard pattern of connections to the linking cable, and the RS232 circuit handles data in a serial form (i.e. one bit at a time) instead of in parallel (i.e. 8, 16, or 32 bits at a time). Terminal software is available for most computers that allows the user to switch the baud rate and other send/receive characteristics, if this is necessary, so permitting communications between different makes of computer and between computers and other equipment such as printers.

Activity

Using suitable communications software and cables, link up two microcomputers, if possible of different types, and transfer between them a text file created on a word processing package. The file should be saved in ASCII format before the transfer, using the appropriate option in the word processing package, and it should be read into a word processor running on the target computer.

Local area networks

More complex than the one-to-one communications link described above are *local area networks*, or LANs. At present there are no universally accepted standards for communications of this type. Acorn and Torch computers, for instance, have their own *Econet* LANs for use with their equipment, and Rank Xerox has pioneered *Ethernet*. Many LANs, including the two mentioned, are based on the *Cambridge Ring*, a type of network developed at the University of Cambridge.

The Cambridge Ring type of network consists of a single cable laid around a site – perhaps one room, or an entire building – with sockets at intervals to which microcomputers can be connected. Each microcomputer must be running network operating system software which includes the communications protocols that allows it to communicate with other devices on the network. In addition, one of the computers must act as 'file server', handling all accesses to any hard disks that may be connected to the network.

A LAN has two main purposes:

1 It allows all computers attached to it to use the software and files stored on the central hard-disk units. This not only reduces the need for large numbers of floppy disks and floppy disk drives, it also ensures that files are always kept up-to-date and all users are working with identical data.
2 It allows a computer to send messages to any other computer on the network, so providing an *electronic mail* facility.

As with other types of digital communications links, the data is sent in packets. There is no switching involved, instead each packet contains the *address* of the receiving device. Each computer connected to the network checks this address, and the one which recognizes the address as its own extracts the packet from the cable and deposits it in its memory. The computer extracts packet after packet in this way until it has assembled the complete message.

145

Activity

Local area networks provide a number of useful facilities besides those mentioned above. You probably have one or more LANs in operation in your college. If so, find out about these facilities – e.g. from any handouts produced for users, and make a list of them for your course notes.

Question

3 Would a LAN be of value to you in your role as youth club leader?

Circuit–switched networks

When a very large number of devices wish to communicate with each other, a circuit-switched network may be more appropriate than a LAN. In this type of network, each device is connected to a switching centre, which handles all message routeing.

The *star network* shown in Figure 6.7 is one type of circuit-switched network, used, for example, where a number of devices are linked by wire to a *host computer*. This computer manages the files and complex

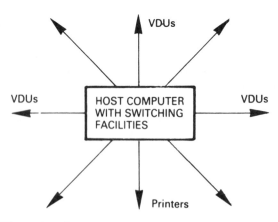

Figure 6.7 Star network

computational tasks as well as allowing one device to communicate with another by setting up temporary direct connections between them. In this latter role, it is acting like a telephone exchange, using a system of switches to connect the two devices so that the call (i.e. the information exchange) can take place.

The connection that is set up by this switching process is completely dedicated to the call, and cannot be used for any other purpose until the call is finished even though, for a significant part of the call time, there will be no information being exchanged.

In telecommunications networks, such as the UK telephone network, there is a number of local switching centres, or exchanges, linked to each other by trunk lines. A long-distance call on such a network must pass through a minimum of two local exchanges.

Packet-switched networks

Circuit-switching suffers from two major disadvantages when applied to telecommunications networks:

- inefficient utilization – circuits are dedicated to individual calls, which means that they are unused during the portions of the call when information is not being exchanged
- engaged lines – one device cannot call another if the latter is itself making a call.

Recently, packet switching has been introduced in telephone networks to overcome these problems, and is replacing conventional circuit-switching. As in LANs, the data is transmitted in addressed packets, each one up to 512 bits long, but in this case the computers controlling the switching centres read the addresses and route the packages. Unlike circuit-switching, lines are not dedicated to individual calls, and some packets that make up a call may travel by a different route to other packets. However, each packet contains information giving its position in the sequence of packets that make up the message, and so it can be properly sequenced upon reaching its destination. If necessary, the network is able to store the complete message until the addressee is available to receive it.

This means that lines can be utilized with much greater efficiency than hitherto, and problems of engaged lines do not occur. Other

147

advantages include the fact that the rate at which data is transmitted can be varied in different parts of the network, which means that:

● the bandwidth can be varied to take account of the volume of traffic and the type of communication link
● devices with different baud rates can inter-communicate via the network.

The Open Systems Interconnection (OSI) reference model

The OSI model defines a set of networking and telecommunications standards. By complying with these standards, different hardware and software manufacturers ensure that their products are compatible. (It is no good attempting to link up different makes of equipment on a network if they are not compatible, as they will not be able to communicate.)

The OSI standards are widely accepted. They divide networking issues into *layers* numbered 1 (the most basic) to 7 (the most complex):

● Layer 1 in the most basic, covering the physical connections. Twisted-wire pairs, coaxial, and optical fibre cabling are all defined by this layer.
● Layer 2 defines protocols, i.e. how the data that travels around the network is to be encoded and decoded.
● Layer 3 defines how data should be routed through the network. Single-channel networks, such as most LANs, do not need this level.
● Layer 4 deals with error handling across the network and flow control.
● Layer 5 defines how communications sessions between network devices are to be managed.
● Layer 6 defines how menus, colours, characters, and so on are to be encoded as control sequences for transmission across the network. SQL, for example, sits within this layer and conforms to it.
● Layer 7 defines how application packages are to use the network.

Broadcast networks

The communications that we have spoken about so far are two-way, or interactive, each party being able to transmit and receive. Broadcast networks, such as those operated by the BBC and IBA, are one-way, meaning that only one party, the broadcaster, is able to transmit.

As explained earlier, the broadcast signals are normally in analogue form, though some, like the Ceefax and Oracle pages put out by the BBC and IBA, are digital. These signals modulate the carrier waves, which are sent by land-line to a transmitting station, from where they are broadcast through the air. They then complete their journey to the receiver in three possible ways:

1 by being picked up directly by a simple aerial attached to the listener's radio or the viewer's TV receiver
2 by being picked up by a special receiving station and routed by cable to the user's receiver
3 by being beamed to a satellite in space for retransmission to earth, where it is picked up by a dish attached to the user's receiver.

Each of these is dealt with below.

Direct broadcasts

In the case of sound radio, these broadcasts are split into AM and FM transmissions. AM has the advantage that it can be broadcast over long distances, its disadvantage being that any electromagnetic noise, such as that produced by atmospheric interference, other stations broadcasting on adjacent carrier wave frequencies, or nearby electrical equipment, cannot be distinguished from the amplitude modulations of the carrier wave, and so is reproduced by the receiver along with the original signal.

Radio transmissions in the short wave band are used for long-distance broadcasting, for they are reflected by the ionosphere, and so can be bent around the earth's surface. The ionosphere itself is affected by the sun, which can break up the radio signal, but evening or night-time transmissions are normally satisfactory.

Short waves are mainly used for radio transmissions aimed at overseas audiences. The BBC, for instance, broadcasts some 600 hours a week in almost 50 languages. In some parts of the world, including Africa and the Middle East, it can boast audiences measured in millions.

For domestic radio programs in this country, FM broadcasts on VHF (very high frequencies, i.e. very short wavelengths) carrier waves give high-quality radio. Not only are these less affected by noise, they provide a high bandwidth and therefore a wide frequency response. Like TV, these broadcasts have a range of only 50 or 60 miles, and so there is no interference from remote stations using the same frequencies.

Some TV broadcasts use VHF transmission. In the main, however, they use UHF (ultra-high frequency) carrier waves with amplitude modulation. The bandwidth has to be very broad to carry the large amount of information that makes up the video and audio signal, some 300 times greater than the bandwidth required for a transmitted radio signal.

Cable broadcasts

These have been used for many years in areas where direct broadcast TV reception is poor. The cable is connected to a favourably located communal TV aerial and then routed to subscribers' homes. In addition to their TV licence, subscribers have to pay a small annual rental to the cable company.

Nowadays, optic fibre cables are often used, and TV broadcasts from satellites may be picked up by communal dishes and fed into the network. The very broad bandwidth of optic fibre means that a large number of TV channels can be carried, as well as specialist services such as pay-TV and business services.

Satellite broadcasts

Unlike short-wave radio broadcasts, VHF and UHF transmissions are not reflected by the ionosphere but instead pass through it. This means that TV transmissions from ground transmitters which are blocked by natural barriers such as mountains are also blocked by the earth's curvature. For this reason, satellites are being increasingly used to carry TV as well as voice and data communications, and it is possible that all TV will ultimately be broadcast this way. For this type of transmission, frequency modulation rather than amplitude modulation is used.

The angular velocity of a satellite orbiting the earth is dependent upon its height. More distant satellites require a lower angular velocity to maintain their orbit, and at one particular height, 22,300 miles from the earth's surface, the satellite circles the earth at a speed which exactly matches the earth's own rotation. So a satellite orbiting the earth, in the same direction as the earth, above the equator at this height appears to be stationary.

Such an orbit is called *geostationary*, and it is important for communications because dishes aimed at satellites in that orbit do not require tracking mechanisms but can be permanently fixed in place. In the UK, satellites in geostationary orbit are fairly low in the southern sky, having an elevation of around 25 degrees.

Two geostationary satellites which are important for TV broadcasts to the UK are:

- Intelsat VA F11, which orbits 27.5 degrees to the west of due south
- Eutelsat 1 F1, which is 13 degrees to the east of south

Future satellites will have high-powered DBS channels (short for *direct broadcasting satellite*). For these, smaller dishes than those required for current satellite transmissions will be required, and different decoding equipment will also be necessary. Most dishes supplied for current transmissions have a diameter of around 1.5 metres, whereas DBS transmissions will require dishes of less than 1 m diameter. Small dishes of this size can normally be erected without local authority planning permission.

The cost of a dish and the associated decoding equipment is currently upwards of around £300 but this price will probably fall with increasing sales. Viewers also need a TVRO (*television receive-only*) licence, which costs £10 for life. Most, however, will not have their own dishes but will instead be linked by broadband fibre optic cable to a communal dish, for which they will pay a small rental.

Broadcasts from these satellites can be picked up all over Europe; so Italians living in this country can receive good-quality Italian TV provided they have a dish and ancillary equipment, and English people living on the continent can likewise pick up broadcasts in their own language. Currently, most of these broadcasts are free, though some are scrambled (i.e. encrypted) and require rental or purchase of special decoding equipment.

Other satellites that can be picked up in this country are the various weather satellites (including Meteosat and the American NOAA satellites) and Uosat, the University of Surrey satellite broadcasting

151

educational material. Meteosat is in geostationary orbit, the NOAA and Uosat satellites are not. These satellites do not broadcast TV signals, but data signals which can be handled by computers such as the BBC micro. The aerial and decoding equipment to receive their transmissions on a BBC costs around £300.

Telecommunications services

The rest of this chapter deals with the main telecommunications services that are available in this country. These include telephone services and cellular radio, telex and facsimile, on-line databases and electronic mail, videotex services, and videophone and video conferencing services. Almost all these services make use of the telephone network.

Telephone

Although the telephone is one of the oldest of these services, it has recently undergone a transformation in terms of developments and related services that have enhanced its usefulness. These include:

- low-cost answering machines for receiving and recording incoming calls
- handsets offering features such as a memory for storing and dialling frequently used numbers and an automatic redial facility for engaged numbers
- computer-based facilities offered by British Telecom's digital exchanges, such as automatic ring-back and tracing of malicious calls
- telephone conferencing so that several parties can be linked together in a single call
- cellular radio so that phones can be used in moving vehicles (see below).

Some new services being developed for subscribers in America but not yet available in the UK are:

- transmission of the caller's telephone number, so that it appears on a screen attached to the recipient's phone. This enables the latter to choose to answer, reject, or forward the call to another number

- call block, allowing recipients to program their phones to automatically reject calls from up to 12 known numbers
- priority screening, which gives priority treatment to calls from up to 12 selected numbers – the phone rings in a distinctive way when a priority number calls, and if the recipient is out, the number is stored in the telephone company's computer for later access by the recipient
- call forwarding, which automatically switches all calls or pre-selected calls to another number
- call answering, which works rather like an answering machine. Subscribers can leave a pre-recorded message on the telephone company's computer, which is automatically relayed to callers. They in turn can leave messages for the subscriber.

Cellular radio

Cellular radio is a computer-controlled mobile communications service made possible by the change-over to digital communications. Under this system, cellular radio sets, or 'mobiles', normally installed in cars, can communicate with each other and with ordinary phone users in the following way.

The country is split up into a large number of 'cells', each one being between 2 and 20 miles across (depending on whether the area covered is urban or rural) and having as its centre a base with a low powered radio transmitter. This is able to transmit to and receive from any mobiles within the perimeter of the cell, and it is connected via a computer-controlled switching centre to the telephone network. Outside the perimeter the strength of the signal falls away, so that although bases in adjacent cells use different frequencies, one in a non-adjacent cell can use the same frequencies without risk of interference.

When a cellular radio subscriber keys in a telephone number, it is transmitted over a special control channel to the cell base, which passes it to the switching centre. The centre dials the number on the telephone network, and at the same time allocates a radio frequency to the mobile, which automatically switches to that frequency and so enables the user to make the call. If the subscriber drives from one cell to another while the call is in progress, the switching centre automatically switches transmitters and frequencies.

In the case of calls made to a mobile, the switching centre sends a paging signal on the control channel. The system will switch the paging transmission from cell to cell until it locates the set, the search being done in an intelligent manner by contacting first the set's home base and looking up the computer records of its last known location. The search time is never more than a few seconds.

Telex

Telex is the most popular way of communicating text over the telephone network, though for reasons which are explained later it is now facing a strong challenge from facsimile.

Telex is generally transmitted and received by *teletypewriters*, which are a kind of communicating typewriter with a paper tape punch and reader. Contact between two teletypes is established by dialling in the usual way, and the text is typed into the transmitting teletype by the telex operator. However, in order to save on telephone line time the message will normally be recorded on paper tape before the call takes place. The receiving teletype is activated automatically on dial-up, and prints the message.

Most major organizations are telex users, and the service can boast well over a million subscribers world-wide. Two important factors have contributed to this success:

1 all telex machines observe common communications standards, i.e. they are all compatible
2 there is a comprehensive directory of telex users.

In the future, however, other text communications services are likely to supersede telex, for its transmission rate is fairly low (50 bits/sec, equivalent to about 66 words per minute), which means that the length of each call, and therefore the phone charge, is relatively high.

Teletex

Teletex is not the same as *teletext*, described later. It is an enhanced telex system designed to take advantage of modern digital packet-switched communications systems. The transmission rate is 2,400 bits per second, almost 50 times faster than telex. Although this system is expected to take over from telex by the end of of the century, its usage is low at the moment because the telex standards have not been precisely specified, and there is some incompatibility between different manufacturers' machines.

Facsimile

Facsimile, or *fax* for short, was developed at the turn of the century to transmit images such as newspaper photographs by telephone line. A fax machine contains a photoelectric cell which scans the image and converts the blacks, greys, and whites into electrical signals and so modulates the telephone carrier wave.

The machine will also act as a receiver, able to decode incoming signals and print them as image on special paper. Nowadays, the images that are handled by fax are often pages of text, which can be scanned and transmitted in the same way.

Fax machines are grouped according to quality of scanning and reproduction. Group 1 machines give very high-quality results, with good differentiation between the various shades of grey. The amount of image information to be transmitted is very high in this case, and the transmission time for an A4 document is six minutes. Group 2 gives lower-quality results but cuts the transmission time in half.

Of most interest so far as text transmission is concerned are the Group 3 and 4 machines, which give black and white results without grey tones. Unlike Group 1 and Group 2, these are digital machines, converting a black (or dark grey) dot on the paper to a binary 1, and a white (or light grey) dot to a binary 0. They are therefore well suited to digital communications, and the transmissioin time – and therefore the cost of each call – is very low. Current models can transmit an A4 page in just a few seconds.

In the past, the use of fax was limited by the lack of a directory of fax users. Furthermore, fax machines differed widely in their transmission rates, and so one manufacturer's models could not communicate with those of another. Today, there is a directory of users (although it is not as comprehensive as the telex directory), and the digital Group 3 and 4 models can communicate with each other. This, together with the high transmission speeds that can now be achieved, has resulted in a rapid increase in fax usage in recent years.

Videotex

Videotex, or *viewdata*, are the terms used to describe computer-based information systems such as Prestel which organize and display text and graphics in the form of an electronic book. The information is held on *frames* or *pages*, each one numbered and linked to other pages so that the user can:

- locate a particular topic by passing through a system of menus (rather as a reader might work through the chapter headings and topic headings in a book)
- locate a particular page by looking up its number and keying in that number (rather as a reader might use the index at the back of a book)
- 'turn' the pages by following a route set up by the page providers (equivalent to reading in sequence the pages in one section of a book).

Computer screens are more difficult to read than books, and in many ways are much less convenient. Why, then, has videotex become so popular as a way of communicating information? The answer is that it attempts to combine the advantages of on-line electronic information storage and retrieval with the ease of use of a book. In common with other electronic information systems, it has the following advantages over paper-based systems:

- a vast amount of information can be stored on the system, and any of it can be rapidly accessed
- the information can be easily and quickly updated without the need to reprint paper documents
- it is available to anyone with access to a telephone line and a suitable terminal
- ancillary services can be provided, such as electronic mail, home banking, and mail order shopping
- in some systems rapid search techniques are available, enabling the subscriber to locate a section of the database simply by typing in a keyword.

There are no universal videotex standards, so it is impossible for, say, an unmodified Prestel terminal in the UK to communicate properly with the French Teletel system. However, Prestel has set a standard followed by many, and there are a number of Prestel-like systems in the UK and on the Continent that you can access with a Prestel terminal or a computer running Prestel-type communications software. Many organizations, for example, run their own Prestel-like viewdata services, providing easily accessed information for branches or dealers, and ordering facilities for customers. The travel industry in particular has adopted the system for booking package tour holidays, and nearly all ABTA members have at least one view-data terminal. Also some schools and colleges and even some individuals operate on-line viewdata systems, and you can access these free of charge.

Prestel and similar systems use *teletext* screen displays, which employ a standard teletext alphanumeric and graphics character set. The size of the display is 40 characters across by 25 lines down, which limits the information displayed to only half that available on the normal 80-column computer screen but which is easier to read on a TV screen. Although quite nice titling and other effects are possible on a teletext screen, true pictures are quite impossible. Teletext has a *block* graphics set, and pictures built up from these are chunky and unrealistic.

The term teletext refers to the non-interactive broadcast system operated by the broadcasting companies using spare line capacity on their TV signals. The broadcast frames can be displayed by teletext TV sets or by the BBC microcomputer with a teletext adaptor. There are at present four teletext channels in this country, corresponding to the four TV channels. Channels 1 and 2 are the BBC's Ceefax service, 3 and 4 are ITV's Oracle.

In Ceefax and Oracle the frames are transmitted in sequence as a *carousel*, the transmission rate being so fast (7 Mbit/sec) that the time needed to cover the entire sequence is only a few seconds. (The time would be a tiny fraction of this if the frames could be transmitted continuously; as it is, the teletext frames have to be slotted in the narrow gaps between each TV frame.) The teletext frames are grouped into sets, each of which has a page or frame number. There are about 100 sets on each channel; on one channel the frames might be numbers 100 – 199, on another 200 – 299, and so on.

The frames that make up a set are broadcast in turn in successive cycles of the carousel, and it can take the viewer two or three minutes to receive and read all the frames that make up a set. To select a set, it is necessary to key in the frame number on a keypad (in the case of TV reception) or keyboard (in the case of computer reception), and then wait as successive frames in the set are received and displayed.

Computer output in the form of software or files of text or data can be sent over videotex systems and picked up by computers with modems or teletext adaptors. The BBC transmits software on

Ceefax, and there is a fair amount of software available on Prestel and other on-line viewdata systems. Some of this software is free, but it is also possible to buy commercially produced packages in this way. It is simply a matter of downloading linked frames containing the software into the computer's memory, and then storing the complete program on disk.

The videotex standards adopted by Prestel and other similar systems were developed in the 1970s and so do not make the best use of the latest technology. As mentioned above, the graphics are poor, and the electronic mail facilities are limited. Also, the transmission rate is slow – 1200 baud for information sent from the Prestel computers, 75 baud for information sent from the user. Prestel has not enjoyed anything like the success that had been predicted for it, and some US videotex systems have been closed down. However, the new integrated digital networks are encouraging the development of much more sophisticated videotex systems, with good graphics and a much higher transmission rate.

Videophones and videoconferencing

Nowadays, it is possible to see as well as hear a telephone caller by using a *videophone*, a device consisting of both a video system and a phone. The video system consists of a black-and-white video camera and a monitor.

An ordinary black-and-white video picture occupies the same bandwidth as 600 telephone conversations. To avoid prohibitively expensive calls, videophone systems transmit pictures intermittently, to give a series of still images rather than a continuously moving one. Also, they remove redundant information from the picture and use compression techniques to reduce the information that has to be sent. The system can be used, for example, to send pictures of components for fault diagnosis, pictures of damaged parts of a patient's body in the health care field, or pictures of products in the field of retailing.

Video conference systems are also available, which allow several callers to hold meetings without needing to travel long distances. British Telecom's Confravision system provides this sort of service, linking major cities by a network of videoconferencing studios for remote meetings.

On-line databases and bulletin boards

There are a large number of on-line systems that can be accessed over the telephone line using a personal computer. The biggest are in the US, but there are a number of important ones in the UK also.

An on-line system may provide *database, bulletin board,* and *email* (i.e. electronic mail) facilities, sometimes just one or two of these, often all three. It may also provide a 'gateway' – i.e. a communications link – to other on-line databases, which you can access from it.

An on-line database mainly stores libraries of economic, financial, and statistical data, together with up-to-the-minute news from sources such as Reuters. It will normally be run on a large computer system, and subscribers will have to pay quarterly fees as well as being charged for the information accessed.

A bulletin board is more like a notice board, containing electronic messages, adverts, and informal 'chatting' and interchange of information by users. It is often a small affair, sometimes run by a single enthusiast using a low-cost computer system. A number of bulletin boards are free, so all you have to pay is the cost of the phone bill.

Systems that charge a fee normally provide a number of services, including email. Each subscriber is provided with an electronic 'mailbox', an area on the host computer's disk where messages from other users can be stored. The subscriber can also send messages to other users, addressing their mailbox by means of their username or number. Like ordinary mail, this kind of system is less immediate than ordinary voice calls but offers a number of advantages:

● there is no interruption factor – you can read all your email and answer them at a time convenient to yourself
● the normal problems of telephone calls – engaged lines and recipient unavailability – are avoided
● it may be cheaper than a phone call, especially if the recipient lives a long way away
● a message can be sent to a number of subscribers at the same time.

Two major UK examples of on-line systems are British Telecom's *Prestel* and *Telecom Gold.* Other smaller systems include:

159

- Easylink, with links between the UK and the US, and ancillary services such as translation of email and telexes into French, German, and Spanish
- Quik-Comm, an international email service
- One To One, with email, translation, noticeboard, radiopaging, as well as access to other databases.

Recently, Compuserve, the enormous US on-line system, has expanded into Europe. This is described below.

Compuserve

In Europe, Compuserve has merged with Datamail, a large email service, and Datastar, a database service, to become Compuserve/FORUM. It is also linked with a number of other email networks, including the UK's JANET academic and research network. Compuserve is accessed via a number of communications networks, one in the UK being Istel.

Compuserve's own on-line service is called the Compuserve Information Service (CIS). This has about 600 000 subscribers, mainly in the US. It includes about 200 special-interest groups or *Forums.* Within a forum, you can leave bulletin-board messages, 'chat' (using the keyboard) with anyone else who happens to be logged on at the same time, and download software. There is a Microsoft Applications forum, for example, and a Lotus forum, as well as forums run by Apple, Atari, IBM, and many others. There are also a number of non-technical forums.

For researchers, CIS provides gateways to some 1400 databases worldwide. For 800 of these, CIS provides its own front end that provides a common method of searching for information. It also offers a flexible email service, allowing you to send not only ASCII text files but also spreadsheet and graphics files, up to 512 K long.

Activity

Some computer magazines publish lists of bulletin boards with phone numbers that are available in the UK. If you have a computer, modem, and communications software, get hold of a list and dial up and explore some bulletin boards.

Electronic data interchange

Increasingly, computers of different organizations are being linked directly over the telephone line, so that ordering and invoicing can be done entirely electronically rather than by sending paper documents through the post. The technology that enables this is called *electronic data interchange* (EDI). The significance of this for business and manufacturing is described in Chapter 9.

EDI requires the provision of what's called *value-added data network services* (VADS). These are services which are added to the basic telecommunications network, and include:

● speed conversion, enabling terminals with differing baud rates to communicate
● protocol conversion, enabling a terminal to communicate with other incompatible terminals
● connection and message-routing facilities
● store-and-forward, allowing messages to be stored for forwarding later
● gateways to other databases and services.

At the time of writing, there are some 5 000 EDI users in Europe out of a total potential market of around 6 million companies, but it is anticipated that EDI usage will grow rapidly during the 1990s.

Assignment 6

Software is available which enables you to set up a viewdatabase – i.e. a Prestel-like information system – on micros such as the BBC micro-computer.

If you have this software available, work in groups to set up a view-database describing a range of bulletin boards, on-line databases, and email facilities that are available for computer users over the telephone network. Each member of the group should select one bulletin board or telecomms service, research it, and produce a set of viewdata frames that describe it. Each of these sets of frames should be accessed via a main menu, and one member of the group should be responsible for producing these together with appropriate introductory frames.

Recap

- In the context of IT, *communications* refers to the transfer of messages in the form of *electromagnetic signals*. If these take place over a short distance, e.g. between two pieces of equipment in the same room, they are called *local communications*. If they take place over a distance, they are referred to as *telecommunications*.

- Telecommunications can be split into two major divisions, namely *radio/TV*, which are mainly intended for audio and video broadcasts, and *telephone networks*, originally designed for voice.

- Local communications, e.g. between two computers, have always been *digital*, but telecommunications have generally been *analogue*. However, digitization has a number of advantages for telecommunications, including:
  - no modems needed for (computer) data transmissions
  - packet switching instead of circuit switching
  - all information, whether voice, image, text, or data, can be sent in a common form and handled by the same equipment
  - the information can be handled by computer, and so computer-based facilities can be offered which would not be possible otherwise
  - dissipation of the signal and noise are minimized
  - systems such as optic fibres offering broadband communications can be used.

  So the telephone networks of many countries are rapidly being digitized, and digital radio and TV is on the horizon.

- A key feature of analogue communications is the use of *carrier waves*, which permit a large number of signals to travel simultaneously through the air or down a wire. The process of superimposing the signal on the carrier wave is called *modulation*, that of extracting it from the carrier wave at the receiver is called *demodulation*. Several modulation methods are possible, including *amplitude modulation*, *frequency modulation*, and *phase modulation*.

- the main types of data communications that take place are *inter-computer communications*, *local area networks*, *circuit-switched networks*, *packet-switched networks*, and *broadcast networks*.

- The telecommunications services that are available in this country over the telephone network include the *telephone*, *telex*, *teletex*, *facsimile*, *electronic mail*, *videotex*, *bulletin boards*, *on-line databases*, *videophones*, and *videoconferencing*.

Answers to questions

1 Your list might include the following:
● listening to radio or TV broadcasts that cover topics of interest to your club
● sending text files such as letters to the printer attached to your computer for printing
● communicating with other youth club leaders by telephone or by electronic mail
● communicating with other people with like interests over a computer conferencing system connected to the telephone network
● sending electronic mail to others via e.g. Prestel
● using CB handsets for certain activities on the Summer camp.

2 Optic fibre cables allow the transmission of a large amount of data per second, giving a rapid transmission rate and reduced telephone charges; a digital technology is employed, pulses of laser light representing binary 0s and 1s, so that conversion between digital and analogue is not required; being digital, the possibility of the signal being degraded is minimized.

3 No. It is intended for offices with a number of computers which benefit from being connected to each other and to central resources such as hard disks and printers. In the role in which you are portrayed, there is only one computer.

7:   Information systems

Objectives

After reading this chapter, you should be able to:
- outline the main phases in the life cycle of an information systems project
- describe the tasks that have to be done to develop a model of an information system
- explain the reasons for using modelling tools such as dataflow diagrams, entity-relationship diagrams, data dictionaries, and process specifications
- use in an elementary way some of the main modelling tools.

Scenario

Introducing computers into your organization can bring many benefits. But if the wrong choices of software and hardware are made enormous damage can be done. It is essential that your organization's information systems are fully studied prior to making any decisions, and that software and hardware are carefully specified.

Introduction to information systems

Examples abound, from hospitals to manufacturing plants, of organizations losing hundreds of thousands and even millions of pounds through purchasing inappropriate computer hardware and software. It's clearly important that an organization's systems are analysed in depth so that the right computerization decisions can be made, and this chapter discusses how to go about this task.

164

A *system* can be defined as a set of procedures that are linked together to perform a task or achieve an objective. The analysis of such systems with a view to computerization is called *systems analysis*, and the task of designing a computerized information system based on this analysis is called *systems design*. The general study of such systems is a branch of computer science called *information systems*.

A large organization is a very complex thing, so it is normal to break down its information system into a number of small, manageable parts or subsystems, and analyse these individually. So systems analysts and designers might begin by computerizing the payroll system, then perhaps the stock control system, and gradually, over a number of years, work through more and more of the subsystems. Throughout this process the analysts will be mindful of the overall system of which these subsystems are just parts, and they will design the subsystems so that they can eventually be linked together to form an integrated whole.

A small organization will not normally go to the expense of getting its software specially written, but will instead purchase off-the-shelf software packages. Some of these are described in the next chapter. You can have these up and running with the minimum of fuss. However, they do require you to modify your ways of working to fit in with their requirements, and considerable problems will result if you make the wrong choices. So even in this case it is necessary to carry out some analysis of the organization's information systems in order to choose the most appropriate software and hardware.

Activity

As youth club leader/summer camp organizer, list four systems in your office that might be analysed with a view to computerization. To start you off, here's one: the summer camp bookings system. (The purpose of this system is to take bookings from members wishing to come to the summer camp, including details of money received from them to pay for the holiday, storing this information, and producing from it various outputs such as the number coming to the camp and the amount of money received.)

The systems project life cycle

The analysis and design of a system is called a *systems project*. It will involve a number of clearly defined phases, which together form the *project life cycle*. These phases are listed below; in traditional (or *classical*) systems analysis and design, they follow each other in sequence.

1 *The survey*, also called *the feasibility study*. This will involve the analyst in extensive interviews with users. Its purpose is: to identify the *scope* of the system, i.e. what parts of the organization are covered by it; to identify the *shortcomings* in the current system; and to determine the *objectives* for the new system, such as the functions it should carry out, and the volume of work it should be able to process in a given time. It will also determine whether it is feasible and cost-effective to computerize the system. At the end of the survey (which will normally take less than 10% of the overall project time), the management will decide whether to proceed with the project, or, if the project does not look cost-effective, to cancel it.

2 *The analysis.* This uses various modelling tools, discussed later in this chapter, to chart the system and from these to develop a detailed specification for the new system. Again, extensive discussions between the analyst and users will take place in order to ensure that these correctly reflect what the system should do.

3 *The design.* This involves allocating different parts of the specification of the new system to different computers or people and splitting up the system into different tasks. In the case of the computerized parts of the system, the program modules that make up each task will have to be designed, as well as any databases that are required (see next chapter for more on databases).

4 *The implementation.* This part of the project is handled mainly by programmers. It involves coding the program modules, testing them to remove bugs, integrating them into the overall system, and then testing to ensure that the modules work together correctly.

5 Further activities include: quality assurance, which involves the final testing of the system; writing down the procedures for the manual parts of the system; entering existing data onto new databases and converting existing databases so that they conform

to the requirements of the new system; and installing the new system.

As I have said, in classical systems analysis and design these phases are carried out in sequence, each one finishing before the next begins (though there is normally some overlap). For example, bottom-level program modules are coded and tested first, higher-level last. However, this approach has been found to have a number of disadvantages, including the following.

- Any mistakes made in early phases are carried through to the later phases, and when they are finally detected they become very expensive and time consuming to correct.
- Trivial bugs are found early on in the project, when the individual program modules are tested, but the most serious bugs are found last, when the modules are linked together and the system as a whole is tested. These serious bugs normally require a great deal of work to eliminate, which can considerably delay the completion of the project and add greatly to its costs.
- If, at implementation time, fundamental problems are found with the initial specification, it's too late to do anything about it.
- No part of the system can be completed and installed until it's all finished. Because of the long time that major projects take to complete – often several years – management can become very impatient and may insist on corner-cutting, resulting in an inadequate and troublesome final system. It also means that if a project is cancelled for any reason before completion, nothing at all is achieved from it.

Because of these problems, what's called the *structured project life cycle* has become popular. In this, the various phases of the project are not carried out in strict sequence, but proceed to some extent in parallel. Any problems encountered in any phase can be fed back to and modify preceding phases. For example, the design phase can throw up problems which may revise decisions reached in the analysis or initial survey phases. On the programming side, high-level modules will be coded and tested early on; where these make use of output from as yet uncompleted lower-level modules, temporary 'dummy' low-level modules are created which simply generate a standard output so that the high-level modules can be tested.

This way of doing things overcomes the problems inherent in the classical life-cycle approach:

- the important high-level errors and mistakes can be found early on in the project, at which point they are easy to correct.
- because some parts of the project are implemented early on, and because all the phases are proceeding more or less in parallel, any problems found at implementation can be fed back to the specification phase, and the specification modified
- some parts of the project will be finished fairly early on, so management can see some tangible results, and even if the project is ultimately cancelled something will be gained.

One of the foremost proponents of the structured approach is Edward Yourdon, and much of the material in this chapter is based on his methodology and terminology. For more information see *Modern Structured Analysis* by Yourdon, published by Prentice-Hall.

Systems analysis

This is the crucial phase in the project life cycle, as it involves analysing the existing system and creating a model of the new system. This model will be developed using a variety of *modelling tools*, i.e. various kinds of diagrams and written text, using either pencil and paper or computers. Much of this chapter deals with these modelling tools.

The classical approach to systems analysis involves the following steps:

1 *Develop the current physical model.* This is a model of the system currently in use, and includes information on the actual technology employed. One modelling tool used in the classical approach is the flowchart, and you may have seen flowchart symbols representing disk drives and other equipment.
2 *Develop the current logical model.* This is abstracted from the current physical model by removing all implementation details such as disk drives and other equipment. It concentrates entirely on flows of data, data stores, originators and receivers of data, and how the data is transformed by processing.
3 *Develop the new logical model.* If the current logical model meets all the user's requirements, i.e. if it handles all the user's

transactions and produces all the outputs needed, then the new logical model will be same as the current logical model. In this case, all that the user requires is a different physical implementation of the system, perhaps replacing manual methods by computerized ones. Normally, though, the current logical model does not do all that the user wants, in which case it must be modified by adding the necessary functionality. New processing capabilities may be needed, new data stores, and new outputs in the form of transaction documents and reports. The result is the new logical model.

4 *Develop the new physical model.* The new logical model contains no physical implementation details. In fact, it assumes perfect technology: whatever processing is required to be done can be done, and done instantly. Life is, of course, never like this, even with computers, and the analyst must decide the best combination of equipment and people to carry out this processing. This involves weighing up the costs and the benefits of the various alternatives, and choosing the most appropriate. Also, the users may want to impose various constraints on the physical implementation, for example they may insist on a fully computerized system, or a wholly manual system, though normally they will opt for something between these two. These implementation details have to be added to the new logical model to develop the new physical model.

This classical approach to systems analysis has a major problem: a great deal of time can be spent producing the current physical model, whereas much of the information contained in it is discarded as it is irrelevant to the final solution. (This is because the logical model excludes all details of the technology employed, as well as all data validation and error checking that has to take place in the physical model due to imperfections in the technology.) Yourdon estimates that as much as 75% of the physical model will be thrown away in the transition to the current logical model. This wasted time occurs at the beginning of the project, and at the stage when users are anticipating some quick answers. They may therefore become impatient and question the need to model the current (obsolete) system, and they may even cancel the project if the delays seem excessive.

Although, due to lack of knowledge of the business, the analyst

169

may require to do some modelling of the current technology just to find out what's going on, Yourdon recommends that the analyst starts, as quickly as possible, to develop the new logical model. He calls this the *essential model* of the system.

The essential model

The essential model shows what the system must do to achieve the user's requirements, but it includes no implementation details (i.e. it says nothing about the technology to be employed, manual procedures, etc.). The model assumes perfect technology, so it also omits procedures that arise from imperfect technology, such as error checking. All such implementation details will be added later, in the transition to the new physical model (which Yourdon calls the *user implementation model*).

The essential model will be constructed using a variety of modelling tools. These tools are often graphical, making use of various kinds of diagram. Some will model the environment of the system, i.e. the people, organizations, and systems from which it receives inputs and to which it gives output, and some will model the processes that must go on inside the system to enable it to handle these inputs and generate these outputs. Yourdon calls these two aspects of the essential model the *environmental model* and the *behavioural model*.

The environmental model consists of the following:

● a description of the purpose of the system
● a context diagram
● an event list.

The behavioural model normally includes:

● dataflow diagrams
● entity-relationship diagrams
● a data dictionary
● process specifications.

These are described in the following sections.

Reasons for using graphical modelling tools

First, let's identify why it's necessary to use this range of modelling tools rather than simply writing everything down in ordinary

English. Up to about 15 years ago that is precisely what systems analysts did: they produced huge documents consisting of hundreds of pages mainly of narrative English describing the user's requirements. These were called *functional specifications* (because they specified the functions of the system). These narrative documents proved to be unsatisfactory, for the following reasons:

● In order to understand the specification you had to read the document from cover to cover. You couldn't study and understand one part in isolation from the rest.

● The same information could be repeated in several places in the document, since it was relevant to different parts of the system. This not only increased the size of the document, it made it more difficult to change, since an alteration in one place needed to be reflected by corresponding alterations in other places.

● Narrative English lacks the precision needed for this kind of work. (Which is one reason why we can't write computer programs in ordinary English, and why mathematics uses its own language of special symbols.) As a result, these documents contained many ambiguities, and they led to misunderstandings which resulted in errors in the final system.

The modern modelling tools listed at the end of the previous section overcome these problems. They have the following characteristics:

● They are mainly *graphic* (pictorial), though they may be supported by some textual material giving additional detail. Unlike text, a picture provides an immediate impression of what's being represented, and can highlight important features at the expense of the trivial. And a picture avoids the ambiguity that is inevitable with ordinary English text.

● They can be *partitioned*, meaning that individual parts of the specification can be portrayed independently of the rest. Unnecessary repetition of information in different parts of the model can be avoided. It is thus possible to study small parts of the system, and, if necessary, modify them, in isolation.

Another advantage of graphical models over huge textual statements is that users can more readily grasp what they show and can therefore verify the accuracy of the analysts' interpretation of what the system is supposed to do.

Let's now look in detail at the modelling tools needed to build the essential model. I'll take them in the order listed in the previous section. As stated there, the first three (the description of the system's purpose, the context diagram, and the event list) make up the environmental part of the model, and the last five make up the behavioural part.

The statement of purpose

Having emphasized the importance of graphical tools, the statement of purpose is not in fact graphical but narrative text! However, it is very short, normally just a few lines long, and simply explains the purpose of the system. This statement is arrived at after interviewing users of the system, and forms a seminal document that should be agreed to by all concerned.

The example I'll be using in this chapter is of a telecommunications billing system (TBS) that might be used by a national telecommunications authority. Its purpose is to charge other telecommunications companies for services provided by the authority. (Those services might include data transmission services, high-speed lines, satellite transmissions for international calls, and so on. The telecommunications companies buying those services then sell them on to the final customer.) Call capture stations owned by these companies handle the various types of call (phone, fax, computer data, etc.), and send the records of these calls (including the user and the timing) to the authority. The TBS within the authority processes the call records in order to bill the companies and produce the various statistics needed to plan and control the services.

The statement of purpose for the TBS might be:

To receive call records from the capture stations and from them to produce the following outputs:
● monthly bills to customers (i.e. the telecommunications companies running the call capture stations)
● credit control documentation in the event of customers not paying on time
● monthly financial reports as well as *ad hoc* reports in order to monitor profitability

● monthly and *ad hoc* statistical information giving e.g. numbers of calls of various types, to help with the forward planning of the business.

Activity

In the activity on page 165 I asked you to list some simple systems in your (youth club) office that might by computerized. In this and the subsequent activities in this chapter I want you to construct various models of just one of these systems. You'll be using these models to produce your assignment at the end of the chapter. For this activity you should choose the system you will be modelling, and write a brief statement of purpose for it. If you choose the camp booking system mentioned in the page 165 activity, your statement of purpose might begin:

To handle information on club members booking on the summer camp, and produce from it various statistics, including . . .

The context diagram

The system as it exists at present is the starting point for the context diagram. However, the purpose of this diagram is to model the interactions that must occur between the *new* system and its environment in order to achieve the aims of the system as written down in the statement of purpose.

The context diagram is in fact a special sort of dataflow diagram (DFD) – I'll be describing DFDs shortly. It consists of a single *process bubble* representing the system as a whole (see Figure 7.1 – the process bubble is the circle in the middle). This processes the various data coming into the system, and produces the various items of information going out. These inputs and outputs are represented on the context diagram by *dataflow* arrows. The organizations/people/systems generating the inputs and receiving the outputs lie outside our system and are called *terminators*, and are represented by rectangles.

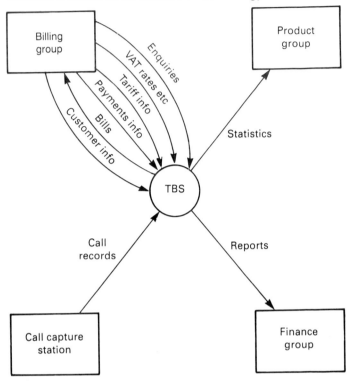

Figure 7.1 Context diagram for the telecommunications billing system

The context diagram for the telecommunications billing system is shown in Figure 7.1. The various terminators in this diagram are:

- the call capture stations, which handle the actual phone, fax, computer, and other calls and generate the call records
- the billing group, a department within the telecommunications authority which liaises with its customers (i.e. the companies running the call capture stations) on billing matters, including forwarding bills to them and receiving payments from them
- the finance group, a department in the authority which oversees all financial matters, including the profitability of its various operations.
- the product group, another department responsible for maintaining and enhancing existing telecommunications products and developing new products.

Activity

Draw a context diagram for the system you chose to model in the previous activity. If you chose the summer camp bookings system, the process bubble will represent this system. The terminators will include the club members (who generate the bookings and pay the cash), the club committee (who may require bookings statistics), and the campsite owners (who want to know numbers coming). Since you will be handling the cash, another terminator will be the bank. Dataflow arrows should be shown in this diagram, and labelled appropriately.

The event list

This lists the events that occur outside the system to which it must respond. These are made up of:

● *flow-oriented events,* i.e. dataflows received from the various terminators, represented by arrows pointing into the system in the context diagram

● *temporal events,* for example the arrival of the end of the month, indicating that the various monthly reports have to be generated (represented by some of the arrows pointing out of the system in the context diagram).

I should also mention a third category of events called *control events.* These do not normally arise in business systems such as the ones studied in this book, but they are important in what are called *real-time systems,* i.e. systems in which the computer must react virtually instantaneously to the information it receives. These include, for instance, factory systems such as process control systems.

So the event list in the case of the TBS system is as follows.

Flow–oriented events from the call capture stations:
   call records.
Flow–oriented events from the billing group:
   customer information, e.g. notification of new customers
   information on payments received
   call tariff information
   currency and VAT rate changes
   enquiries.

175

Temporal events:
  request bills
  request monthly statistics and financial reports.

The statement of purpose, the context diagram, and the event list together make up the environmental model. This describes the purpose of the system in the larger scheme of things and shows the interactions that take place between the system and its environment.

Activity

Write down the event list for the system you chose to study in previous activities. Base your list of flow-oriented events on the inward-pointing dataflow lines on your context diagram, and base the list of temporal events on the reports in that diagram (some of the outward-pointing dataflow lines).

Dataflow diagrams

The first step in the production of the behavioural model is often to draw dataflow diagrams (DFDs). As their name implies, these chart the flow of data through the system. We have already looked at a special sort of dataflow diagram which models the system as a whole in its environment: this is the context diagram, and it represents the entire system by a single process bubble.

What we must now do is look at what happens inside this single process bubble. We must break it down into a number of subsidiary process bubbles, linked to each other by dataflows. Often many of these subsidiary bubbles can be broken down still further. What we end up with is various *levels* of dataflow diagram: level 0 is the context diagram; level 1 shows the major processes in the system drawn as bubbles on a single sheet of paper (normally A4); level 2 is a series of dataflow diagrams, one for each of the level 1 bubbles. Each of these should be drawn on a separate sheet of paper, and show the breakdown of that bubble into subsidiary bubbles linked by dataflows.

This levelling process continues for as long as necesary, depending on the complexity of the system. A simple system, such as the one you are developing in the accompanying activities, may consist of a single (level 1) DFD. A complex system may be broken down into many DFDs occupying three or four levels.

Exactly how the processes are split into bubbles and levelled is to some extent arbitrary, but as a rule there should be around six bubbles in an individual DFD. This makes a DFD easy to understand, as well as ensuring that it can be drawn on a single sheet of A4 paper; or, in the case of a computerized modelling tool, displayed within the confines of a computer screen.

The context diagram shows only inputs to and outputs from the system as a whole, together with their terminators in the system's environment. It does not show the storage of data within the system: this, after all, is nothing to do with the system's environment and should therefore not appear in the environmental model. Now, however, we are looking at the insides of the system and its behaviour, and so we must show the storage of data. Data stores can be represented in various ways, including the parallel lines and rounded boxes. The DFDs in this book use the former, as shown in Figure 7.2. The TBS stores represented there hold the data on calls, call capture stations, customers, tariffs, currency and VAT rates, bills and payments.

Each store will be linked to the process bubbles that use it by means of dataflow arrows. Arrows directed into a store represent data being written to it, arrows directed out of the store represent data being read from it.

Note that all the dataflow arrows in a DFD should be properly labelled, as illustrated in the context diagram in Figure 7.1. Labels are omitted from Figure 7.2 to reduce the complexity of the figure.

The first step in constructing the set of levelled DFDs is to produce an overall or *first-cut* DFD showing every process in the system and every store. This should have one process bubble for each event in the event list. In effect, it is the context diagram with the single process bubble broken down into its subsidiary processes, dataflows, and data stores. The first-cut DFD for the TBS is shown in Figure 7.2. You should study it carefully, following the dataflows through the various processes and data stores.

Next, the first-cut DFD has to be levelled. This will involve first, grouping various process bubbles together in order to produce the level 1 DFD (this is called *upwards levelling*), and second, in the case

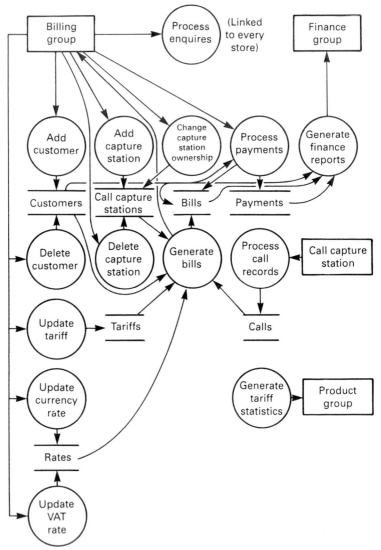

Figure 7.2 First-cut DFD for TBS

of bubbles that represent complex series of processes, breaking them down into subsidiary bubbles (this is called *downwards levelling*). In Figure 7.2, the 'Add customer', 'Delete customer', 'Add call station', 'Delete call station' bubbles, for example, will be combined into a single bubble for the level 1 DFD, and the bubbles representing generating bills, which is a complex task, will be expanded into several bubbles in a level 2 DFD.

Each bubble in the DFDs should be numbered, for ease of reference. Level 1 bubbles are numbered simply 1, 2, 3, etc. If the bubble labelled 1 is broken down into subsidiary bubbles in a level 2 DFD, these will be numbered 1.1, 1.2, 1.3, etc. If bubble 1.1 is broken down into further subsidiary bubbles in a level 3 DFD, these will be numbered 1.1.1, 1.1.2, 1.1.3, and so on.

Activity

Draw the first-cut DFD for the system you are modelling in the activities in this chapter. Note that each event in your event list must correspond to one process bubble. Since you are modelling a very simple system, there is probably no need to refine this DFD to cover several levels – in other words, it can form your level 1 DFD, no level 2 DFDs being necessary.

The entity–relationship diagram

Entity-relationship diagrams (ERDs) model the *data* that's stored in the system. They show the relationships between the stores. Each store (represented by parallel lines in the DFD) is an ERD *object*, and is represented by a rectangular box in the ERD. Relationships between the stores are represented by diamond-shaped boxes. Figure 7.3 shows the ERD for the TBS system discussed in previous sections.

Various conventions are used in ERDs. I've chosen to use plain lines to link relationship diamonds with objects (stores), and 'N' to indicate a one-to-many relationship, e.g. one customer responsible for many calls.

Activity

Study Figure 7.3 carefully, then try to draw an ERD for the system you are modelling in these activities. Note that each store in your DFD should correspond to one ERD object.

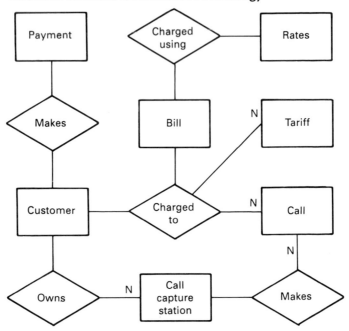

Figure 7.3 Entity-relationship diagram for the TBS system

The data dictionary

Suppose one of the data stores in the DFD you drew in an earlier activity was 'Club members'. What data would you hold in this store? Obviously the member's *name*, his or her *address*, *telephone number*, *date of birth*, and perhaps other items of data besides. These are the *data elements* into which the data item (record) 'member' might be decomposed. If you wished, you might decompose some of these data elements further – for example, 'name' might be decomposed into *title*, *forename*, and *surname*.

It is necessary to include in the behavioural model this breakdown of the data used by the system. This is called the *data dictionary*. It defines what is contained in the various stores (we need to know this in order to design the databases used by the system), and it ensures that we know precisely what the inputs and outputs of the system contain.

Besides listing the data elements, the data dictionary also indicates which are the *key* elements, i.e. which are used to uniquely identify an item (record) of data. If your club is fairly small, the element 'name' might be used as the key, as no two members have the same name. In a large organization, however, names might be duplicated, in which case you would want to assign each member a unique number and use this as the key. The data dictionary will also show the breakdown of each data element into its smallest components, which might be alphabetical characters, numbers, or other symbols; programmers need this information when they come to implement the system.

Various conventions are used by analysts when constructing data dictionaries. A common one uses the following symbols (which are fairly standard in other branches of computer science):

= is composed of
+ and
[] select one of several choices – each choice being separated by |
{} iteration, i.e. repeat as needed
() optional, i.e. can be included as and when necessary
@ key element
** comment.

Using these symbols, the element *name* in our club members data store might be defined as follows:

Name =   title + forename + surname
title =   [Mr|Mrs|Miss|Ms|Dr]
forename =   {legal-character}
surname =   {legal-character}
legal-character = [A-Z|a-z|0-9|'|-| |]

As you can see, each component of the data element is successively broken down into its final indivisible components. When you remember that each item in each data store must be broken down into elements in this way, you can see that the data dictionary can be quite a large document.

Here's the data dictionary entries for the store 'calls' in the TBS system shown in Figure 7.2. Note that this section of the dictionary begins with the name of the store in upper-case (CALLS), which is composed of repeated occurrences of the data item (record) CALL. Note too the convention that can be used for specifying the minimum and maximum number of characters in an iteration: enter the minimum number before the '{'and the maximum after the'}'. In these examples the minimum equals the maximum, meaning that there must be exactly that number of iterations.

CALLS =	{CALL}
CALL =	*information about a call*
	@call-id + phone-number + customer-id +
	start-time + end-time
call-id =	*identification of a call*
	{legal-character}
phone-number =	*incoming call phone number*
	{numeric-digit}
Start-time =	*starting time of a call*
	units: hours, minutes, seconds
	4{numeric-digit}4 + : + 2{numeric-digit}2
end-time =	*finishing time of a call*
	units: hours, minutes, seconds
	4{numeric-digit}4 + : + 2 {numeric-digit}2

(*legal-character* and *numeric-digit* are defined elsewhere in the dictionary so don't need defining here.)

Activity

Write down the data dictionary entry for one of the stores shown in your DFD drawn earlier.

Process specifications

The process specifications will form the largest part of the behavioural model. One must be drawn up for each DFD process bubble, and defines what that process has to do to transform the data inputs it receives into outputs. These process specs can be read by users to verify that the system will perform in the required manner, and they will form the basis of the programming that will be done to implement the system.

Various modelling tools are used for this task. Some are graphical, including decision tables, while others are narrative. *Structured English* is often used, this being an exact form of ordinary English with a restricted and tight vocabulary. It results in a process spec which reads rather like a PASCAL program.

Here's part of a structured English process specification that might used to define the process 'generate bills' in Figure 7.2:

go to first call record for this customer
set **amount** to 0
DO WHILE there are more records for this customer
   multiply **call-duration** by **charge-rate**
   add result to **amount**
   go to next record
ENDDO
print **amount** on invoice

Designing and implementing the system

The above sections describe what's involved in developing the essential model of the system. Implementation details now have to be added to produce the new physical model, or what Yourdon refers to as the user implementation model. These details are added to the essential model by annotating its various diagrams, such as the DFD and ERD.

It is at this point that the technological choices have to be made. These depend on the relative costs and benefits of the various options, and the user's own wishes. Some parts of the essential model will be automated, other parts may be carried out by people. Where people interact with computers, i.e. at the points of input and output, the various input/output devices must be specified, forms and screen displays designed, and help messages and error messages written.

Next comes system design. This task may be carried out by the systems analyst(s), or by a separate team of system designers. It involves developing two models:

1 *The systems implementation model*, consisting of a *processor* model which decides how the various parts of the essential model should be allocated to different computer processors, and a *task*

model which allocates the various processes and data stores to individual tasks running on each processor.

2 *The program implementation model*, which specifies the program modules needed to carry out the functions indicated by the process bubbles and detailed in the process specifications.

Next comes coding, in which the programmers write the program modules specified in the program implementation model. They will be guided by the process specifications contained in the essential model. These program modules, when written, have to be tested both individually and when they are finally combined into a complete system. For this, suitable test data must be generated, and the essential model should contain enough information to decide on a suitable set of data to test the various demands that will be made on the system.

Then, procedure descriptions have to be produced for the manual parts of the system, new databases must be set up or existing databases converted, and, when everything is ready, the final system installed. Installation may involve an overnight switch, or a gradual changeover as different groups of people receive documentation and training in the new system.

Assignment 7

Use the work done in the activities in this chapter to develop the essential model of one of the youth club/summer camp office systems (or as much of this model as you can). You should include a statement of purpose, context diagram, event list, dataflow diagram, and entity-relationship diagram. You should also include a data dictionary for just one of the data stores. Then have a go at developing the user implementation model of the system, specifying what equipment should be used, and which processes should be automated and which should be manual.

Recap

● A system is a set of procedures linked together to perform a task. *Systems analysis* involves the study of such systems with a view to computerization.

● The life cycle of a systems project involves a number of phases. In modern structured analysis these phases proceed more or less in parallel. They include the initial *survey* or *feasibility study*, the *analysis*, the *design* of the new system, the *implementation* of the new system (mainly the coding and testing of the program modules), and further activities such as *quality assurance, writing manuals,* and *database conversion.*

● The main task of modern structured analysis is the development of the *essential model.* This shows what the system must do to achieve the user's requirements, but includes no implementation details. It consists of two parts: the *environmental model,* which shows the interaction of the new system with its environment, including the information inputs received from the environment and the information outputs flowing to the environment; and the *behavioural model,* which shows what must go on inside the system in order to process the inputs to produce the outputs.

● A variety of *modelling tools* are used to create these models, many of them graphical. The environmental model consists of a *description of the purpose of the system,* a *context diagram* showing the information flowing between the system and its environment, and an *event list* showing the events that occur outside the system to which it must respond.

● The behavioural model will include: *dataflow diagrams,* showing the flow of data through the system, the processes, and the data stores; an *entity-relationship diagram* modelling the stored data by showing the relationships between the stores; a *data dictionary* listing the data elements that make up the stores and showing their composition; and *process specifications* which define what each process in the system must do in order to transform the data inputs it receives into outputs.

● Implementation details are added to the essential model to produce the *user implementation model.* This may be done by annotating the dataflow diagrams and other models. It is at this point that the technological choices are made, by comparing the costs and benefits of different options. It is at this point too that the user's wishes are taken into account regarding what parts of the system should be automated and which parts should be carried out manually. Screen displays, data entry forms, and other parts of the human–computer interface are designed at this time also.

● Next comes systems design, which involves the development of two models. The first is the *systems implementation model,* which consists of a *processor model* showing how the various parts of the essential model should be allocated to different processors, and a *task model* which allocates the processes and data stores to tasks running on these processors. The second is the *program implementation model*, which describes the program modules that must be created to carry out the processes identified in the essential model.

● The program modules are coded and tested, then integrated to produce the complete system. This also must be tested, procedure description covering the manual parts of the system written, and the final system installed.

8:   IT in the office

Objectives

After reading this chapter, you should be able to:
- outline the main implications and benefits of applying information technology to the work of the office
- describe the main types of computer and other hardware used for office IT
- describe the facilities offered by the main types of office software, including record-keeping software, spreadsheet software, business graphics software, word processing and desktop publishing software

Scenario

Computers can automate much of the routine work of the office, including your youth club administrative procedures referred to in earlier chapters. But what are the features and facilities offered by the computer for record keeping, word processing, graphics, and so on, how are they used, and what benefits do they bring?

Office automation

The term *office automation*, or OA for short, is used to describe the application of the computer and related devices to the work of the office. Unlike the automation of other parts of industrial enterprises, the automation of the office has happened only recently, within the last decade.

Factory automation has long been a feature of the industrial scene, and large equipment feeding huge production lines has boosted the productivity of factory workers and created much of the wealth of the industrialized world. The automation of routine clerical jobs such as payroll, stock control, invoicing, purchase records, and financial accounting procedures has also been going on for a long time, ever since the introduction of large and expensive punched card equipment early in this century.

The reason why the world of the manager, the administrator, and the secretary has been so long unaffected by these developments is simply that the equipment was so large and expensive that it could only be economically used for large routine jobs with long production runs – such as generating hundreds of invoices or thousands of pay-slips – which is not what the jobs of managers and secretaries are like. Their jobs are very varied. Managers' jobs involve getting information together from many sources in order to make decisions on a variety of topics, and putting those decisions into effect. Secretaries' jobs involve a variety of supporting activities such as writing letters, keeping diaries, and making appointments.

The automation of highly varied jobs of this sort had to await the advent of low-cost microcomputers that could economically be used for small-run office jobs, supported by spreadsheet, word processing, diary management and other office software. The most popular microcomputers are IBM PCs and compatibles, of which there are some 10 million worldwide, but other types of microcomputers or *workstations* dedicated to specialized applications such as word processing or computer-aided design are also widely used.

The benefits and implications of office automation

The economic benefits of automation are enormous. In the 20-year period between 1960 and 1980, for example, there was a substantial investment in factory equipment which resulted in the doubling of factory workers' productivity. During the same period only one tenth of the amount was invested per person in the office, with the result that office productivity remained almost static during this period. The result was that office costs soared from 40% to over 60% of total business costs during that period. Now, with the coming of micro-computers into the office, office productivity can catch up.

Besides the savings in costs that computers can bring, there are quality benefits also:

● Computers don't make mistakes, so provided that data is keyed in correctly, the results will be correct.

● Once the data has been keyed in, many different kinds of analyses can be carried out at almost no additional cost, so that much more management information can be produced. For example, sales data can be analysed in many different ways, by product, by geographical area, by type of customer, and by salesperson, to assist management decision-making.

● Computers work at very high speeds, and so information and analyses can be produced almost instantly. Reports that in the past might take weeks or months to produce, may now be available at the press of a key.

Automation does, of course, mean the replacement of human work by that of the machine, and this has profound social implications, which are explored in the final chapter. There are implications for the level of unemployment in the country, and for the quality and types of jobs that are available for those in employment. So far as office employment is concerned, things look reasonably hopeful:

● Increased productivity means either that the same volume of work will be produced with less staff, or that the same staff will produce more, or some combination of both. Fortunately, the advent of the computer has coincided with a substantial growth in the volume of office work, and office employment figures remain buoyant.

● Computers have not, in themselves, led to a deterioration in the quality of office employment. Many office workers have nicer and more interesting jobs, involving more responsibility and a wider range of activities, as a result of computers. Where the reverse is the case, it is often the result of computers being introduced badly, with no consideration being given to job design, and little thought being given to ergonomic factors such as screen positioning and chair design.

Questions

1 What do you think are the benefits and implications of office automation for you in your role as youth club leader?
2 Many items of equipment besides computers are associated with modern office systems. One example is the photocopier. From what you have learned so far on this course, name five others.

Office automation systems

The computer is the main item of office automation equipment, although other equipment such as scanners, laser printers, and modems are used, often linked to the computer. Where a number of computers are used on a site, they may be linked up, so that messages and files can be passed electronically from one user to another, and so that hardware resources can be shared. A variety of computer configurations are in fact possible, the main types being stand-alone microcomputers such as PCs, networked microcomputers, and multi-user systems.

Stand-alone microcomputers

'Stand-alone' means that the computer is self-contained, and does not share the hard disk, processor, or other parts of another computer system. The most common example of this type of system is the IBM PC and compatibles, though other kinds of workstations such as dedicated word processors are also used. Stand-alone systems are used in small offices, or by individuals in larger organizations whose work is self-contained and who have therefore little or no need to link into wider systems.

Networked microcomputers

In many larger offices a local area network offers many advantages. In this, each computer is linked by cable to other computers in the office and perhaps in other parts of the building, giving each one access to central hard disk and printer facilities, and being able to send messages to any other computer on the network.

This can achieve economies, since hard disk and other resources are shared. More important, though, are the additional facilities a network offers users:

- access to common files, so that any updating carried out by one user is instantly available to all
- electronic mail facilities between networked computers
- automatic backup of files at the end of each day by the network manager, so reducing the risk of losing data.

Multi-user computers

In this, a number of terminals are linked to a host computer, each one having access to its processing power and to its hard disk and other peripherals. The terminals can be *dumb*, i.e. keyboard-and-screen units lacking any processing power of their own, or *intelligent*, i.e. possessing their own processing power. PCs are sometimes used as intelligent terminals.

This set up offers similar advantages to a network, but the host computer is normally much more powerful than the ordinary PC and therefore able to run more powerful software. IBM ATs and compatibles have multi-user capabilities, being able to support up to three terminals, but they are rarely used in this role. Normally, a more powerful type of computer known as a *mini-computer* is used as the host, and this is able to support more terminals as well as offering more powerful processing. A mini is a cut-down version of very large *mainframe computers*, so-called because of the large metal frame that housed the processor in early models. This type of computer is very powerful indeed, able to support dozens of terminals, but its price is such that it is a cost-effective acquisition for only the largest organizations.

Office automation and the paperless office

It has long been predicted that office automation, with its electronic storage and retrieval systems, will end the use of paper for memos, letters, reports, etc. However, this prediction is still far from being realized in most organizations, and even where computers are well entrenched there is usually no lack of paper-based documents. The contrary is often the case.

Nevertheless, some large companies have installed workstations on the desks of every office worker, so that all internal correspondence is sent by electronic mail systems rather than by paper. And office systems are now appearing that are designed reduce severely, if not end, the use of paper.

One example is Wang's *Integrated Imaging System*, which is a capture, archiving, indexing, and retrieval system for all non-computerized information, such as letters and other documents. This system works by:

● capturing images of the documents using a scanner
● transferring them to the host computer, where they are stored on Worm optical discs (i.e. optical discs which allow you to write the data in a non-erasable form)
● handling them like any other computer-based information, i.e. retrieving them, passing them to workstations such as PCs which are connected to the host computer, and so on.

Office automation software

The main types of software used for office automation applications are:

● database software for record-keeping applications
● spreadsheet software for applications involving tables of data
● business graphics software for presentations
● word processing and desktop publishing software for letters, brochures, etc.
● communications software for electronic mail and to access on-line databases
● personal productivity software, such as diary systems and electronic notepads
● other software, such as project and expert systems.

All these are dealt with in the sections below, apart from communications software (covered in Chapter 6) and expert systems (covered in Chapter 9). In most sections, I shall adopt the following general pattern, which will be to:

● introduce the application
● discuss the main concepts underlying the application
● outline the main tasks that have to be done
● describe how the application is used in practice.

Database software

A *database* is a set of data organized into records. A software package which allows you to organize data in this way is called a *database management system* (DBMS). There are two types of database software:

- packages which are able to handle just one file of records at a time, sometimes called *cardbox* or *flat-file* packages
- *relational database* packages, which are able to handle several files at a time, and to build up links (or relationships) between files.

Relational databases are needed for more complex applications. One such application is invoicing, where customer details (such as the name and address) have to be extracted from the customer file, and product details (such as the price) have to be extracted from the stock file (see below). Relational databases can be (and often are) used for single-file applications, but being more complex than flat-file packages, they may make those applications unnecessarily difficult.

To illustrate the difference between flat-file and relational databases, I'll enlarge on the invoicing application mentioned in the previous paragraph. This may have two main files:

- the customer file, which has one record per customer with his or her name and address, and onto which you enter details of all orders received from customers – the products purchased, the price, the date of purchase, and so on
- the product file, which has one record per product line, holding details such as the price, quantities received from suppliers and dates, quantities issued to customers and dates, the balance in stock and so on.

You can imagine that the job of the invoicing clerk would be made very efficient if, when he or she keys in the customer code number, the code number of a product purchased, and the quantity, the computer automatically displays both the customer details and the product details, and updates both the customer file and the product file with the relevant details of the transaction. That is exactly what a relational database does – it links files together, so that information from both can be displayed or printed, and enabling both to be updated.

Often, more than two files will be linked in this way. In the above sales situation, for instance, there may be three files:

- an order file containing details of the order (the customer's code number, the product code numbers and quantities, and the date), from which the total order value is calculated and invoices and delivery notes produced

● a customer file containing the customer's name and address, together with the values of orders and their dates, from which the monthly statement is produced

● a product file containing the product details such as quantities received and issued, and from which purchase orders are produced to send to suppliers.

The order file picks up the customer details from the customer file, and the product details from the product file. It in turn updates the customer file with the value of the order, and the product file with the number of issues.

This is a simplified description of what actually goes on in a sales accounting situation, but it illustrates the value of relational databases.

Client/server database architecture

In some of the more advanced database systems the task of data storage is separated from the task of processing the data. The former is carried out by *server* software, while the latter is carried out by the *client* package. The server software normally resides in a mainframe or minicomputer, or perhaps on a network server, and it handles basic data storage tasks. The client can be any database package that is able to accept data from the server; it provides the user interface as well as the various input and output facilities. Other kinds of application package, such as spreadsheets, can also act as clients. The server software is also referred to as the *back end*, and the application software is referred to as the *front end*.

In recent years *Structured Query Language* (SQL) has become important. This is a database language that allows clients to communicate with servers. The client sends instructions to the server in this language, one example being the instruction to find all records that match certain criteria. Normally, the user can simply select a menu choice offered by the client, and the software generates the necessary instructions. Often, the client package will also allow the user to type the commands directly, should he or she so wish. The data will be retrieved by the server, passed to the client, and will appear at the right place in the application (which might be a spreadsheet or word processed document) as though it had been typed in.

A number of (client) application packages now support SQL and can therefore make use of server software. They include Paradox and DataEase. SQL is also available for Excel, Microsoft's spreadsheet package. Two well-known and powerful SQL servers are Oracle and Ingres.

Record-keeping concepts

Let's turn now to the main record-keeping concepts. These are *data, file, record, field,* and *template.*

Data
The purpose of record keeping is to store, retrieve, and analyse data on a variety of topics. Some data is numbers, examples being ages, prices, and quantities. Other data, however, is alphabetic or alphanumeric information such as names or postcodes.

File
A record-keeping package enables you to set up files to store data on a variety of topics. For example, you might keep one file containing names and addresses, another containing details of customers' orders, and another containing details of stock held in your department. Not only does the type of data differ from file to file, but the way in which it is organized, or structured, differs also.

So a file created by a record-keeping package is an organized body of data, or *database*.

Record
A record is a single unit of structured data in a file. In a name-and-address file, for example, a record is the data relating to one individual, organized as in the following way:

the name
several lines of address
the telephone number.

All the records in a file have an identical structure. That structure serves the same purpose as the printed design on the cards in a card index. The data varies from record to record, but the structure remains the same.

Field

A field is the space in a record occupied by a single item of data, such as a name, or a line of an address, or a price, or a quantity. The set of fields, and the spaces allocated to them, determine the structure of a record.

Template

A template is the structure of a file without the data. When you create a file, your first task is to design the template. It's a bit like designing the printing that is to go on the cards in a card index. You decide the fields you need, their position, the space to be allocated to each, and any labels (names) that you are going to give them. In the case of a computer-based system, you can build other things into your design, such as automatic date-stamping when a record is added to a file, automatic calculation of balances and totals of numeric fields, and automatic checks on the validity (i.e. reasonableness) of the data when it is entered.

Figure 8.1 shows a demonstration template for a student record system. (A real-life template would be bigger, with more subjects.) There are fields, and field labels, to record the name, address, and other personal details of each student, more fields in the boxes in the lower half of the template to enter assignment and exam grades for the various subjects, and a final field at the bottom for the tutor's comments. In this template, the student's average grades are automatically recalculated whenever assignment grades are added to his record. The software package used to create this file, Q&A, allows the template to be programmed so that this sort of feature is easily built in.

The computer displays this template on the screen whenever a record is added to the student record file, allowing you to add data into each field. When you retrieve the record later on, the template is again displayed, together with that record's data.

Record-keeping tasks

The tasks that need to be carried out on a file are as follows.

Designing the file

Before you can keep records, you must first of all design the template and other parts of the record-keeping system. It's worth taking some

Demonstration Student Records

Surname:
Street:
Postcode:

Forename:
Town:
Phone:

DOB:
County:

Dept:

Course:

Year:

Tutor:

SUBJECT	1	2	3	4	5	6	7	8	9	10	AV	EXAM
English												
Mathematics												
Gen. Studies												

Comments

Overall average

Figure 8.1 Template for student records file

trouble over this task, as you only have to carry it out once. Templates designed for one file can often be used for others, though perhaps with some modification.

Adding and deleting records

Once the template is designed you can start adding records to your file. From time to time you will need to add more new records, and you will need to delete from the file old records which are no longer required. In the case of the student records file, many new records have to be added at the start of each year, and the records of students who have left deleted.

Updating records

You need to keep records up to date by adding new data to them. For example, you need to enter stock movements in the case of a stock file, or assignment grades in the case of student records. You may also need to amend data which is no longer correct, as when the price of a stock item changes, or a student moves to a new address.

Validating data

Because of the risk of human error, you need to build into your system at the template-design stage automatic checks on the validity, or reasonableness, of the data that you enter. This may mean checking that it lies within a certain range, or that it is of the right type, e.g. textual, or numerical.

Searching records

You need to be able to locate individual records, perhaps to deal with queries. For example, you may need to look up the record of a a student to check his performance; or to look up a particular stock item to check the balance in stock. You also need to be able to find all records that conform to certain criteria. For example, you may want to find all students who achieved less than a certain mark in English, or all stock items with stock balances below the reorder level.

Sorting records

You may also wish to sort the records in a file into order. For example, you may want to list student records alphabetically by name, or in order of overall grade.

Calculating

There is a variety of calculations you may wish to carry out on the records in a file. You may wish to update stock balances each time there is a stock movement, or calculate the total value of all stock held.

Reporting

You will also need to produce periodic reports which summarize the data held in a file. In the case of the student records, for example, you may want to know the average marks achieved by the class for each assignment, in order to check out the effectiveness of the teaching and assignment program. In the case of the stock records, you may want to produce reorder lists of stock that is running out, or a summary of stock movements by category of stock.

Database applications

Databases are useful at both the managerial and clerical levels in an organization. At the managerial level they are a decision-support tool, for reports can be produced from them which summarize what's going on and give pointers for the future. At the clerical level they provide an easy way of entering and retrieving data, and dealing with enquiries.

So in many situations a clerk will require access to a database to carry out the latter type of task, and a manager will require access to it to get out a report. Where personal computers are used, this may mean two or three people having access to the same PC, or else setting up a configuration of multi-user or networked PCs.

Some database applications are almost exclusively clerical, an example being a name-and-address file. Most database applications, though, have both clerical and managerial elements.

Typical business database applications include:

- stock records
- personnel records
- customer records
- accounts
- mailing-lists
- survey data.

Activity

Use a record-keeping package to create a simple name-and-address system that you might use for the members of your youth club. Enter some names and addresses, and try out the various facilities that the package provides, such as sorting the records into order, searching for particular records and groups of records, and calculating summaries of the data. Save your work onto disk, and produce a print-out of the data.

Spreadsheet software

Introduction to spreadsheets

A spreadsheet is a software package which organizes data in the form of a table or *worksheet*. An example of a worksheet is shown in Figure 8.2. This is a simple cash–flow forecast for a small business. As you can see from this example, it is mainly with numbers, and calculations on numbers, that spreadsheets are concerned.

In this worksheet, if you alter any of the income or expenditure data, the computer immediately and automatically recalculates the cash–flow forecast on the bottom lines. As anyone who has had anything to do with cash–flow forecasts will testify, this is much better than having to do the job manually.

Spreadsheets have some similarities with the record-keeping packages described in the last chapter, and you can think of a worksheet as a file of records listed in tabular form:

- each column in a worksheet corresponds to a field in a record
- each row corresponds to a record
- programming statements can be inserted so that calculations are carried out automatically.

(You can, in fact, read a set of records prepared in a database package such as Q&A into a spreadsheet package such as Lotus 1-2-3, and the records will be listed in worksheet form. Or you can read a Lotus worksheet into Q&A, and each row becomes a separate record.)

Spreadsheet concepts

Spreadsheets share a number of concepts with record-keeping packages, including the concepts of *file*, *data*, *label*, and *template*. Concepts that are special to spreadsheets, which are dealt with below, are *column*, *row*, *cell*, *formula*, and *window*.

Cash-flow forecast for Pine Workshop, Jan–June 1992

	JAN	FEB	MAR	APR	MAY	JUN
INCOME						
Sales	9500	10000	10500	11000	11000	11500
Other	2000	1000	1500	1300	1500	1500
Total	11500	11000	12000	12300	12500	13000
EXPENSES						
Wages	3300	3500	3700	4000	4000	4200
Stock	3000	3000	3000	3300	3300	3500
Rent	1200	1200	1200	1200	1200	1200
Rates	400	400	400	400	400	400
Fuel	350	350	350	300	300	300
Other	1000	1000	1200	1200	1200	1200
Total	9250	9450	9850	10400	10400	10800
B/F	10000	12250	13800	15950	17850	19950
BALANCE	12250	13800	15950	17850	19950	22150

Figure 8.2 Cash-Flow forecast worksheet

Column

A worksheet is split vertically into columns, which can correspond to the fields in a database. The default column width is typically 9 characters, though this can easily be altered either globally (i.e. across the entire worksheet) or for individual columns. Most spreadsheet packages will cope with worksheets running into hundreds of columns, though the number you can actually use depends upon the amount of RAM in your computer.

Columns are normally identified by letters, starting A, B, C, . . ., and continuing through AA, AB, AC, . . ., BA, BB, BC, and so on. To make the worksheets you design easy to read, you should label each column by typing a heading at the top. In Figure 8.2, the column labels are the months of the year.

Row

A worksheet is also split into rows, i.e. horizontal lines of data which can correspond to the records in a database. Rows are numbered downwards, starting at 1. Most spreadsheet packages will, in theory, permit worksheets extending to several thousand rows, though in practice the number you can use depends on your computer's RAM. To make your worksheet design easy to read, you should normally type in row labels at the left, as is done in Figure 8.2.

Cell

A cell is the space occupied by an individual item of data in a worksheet. It is identified by the column letter and row number in which it lies. For example, the cell lying at the intersection of column C and row 4 is called C4.

Formula

Besides data, a cell can contain a programming statement, or *formula*. These are not visible when you are entering data, but they reside in the background. A formula normally involves a mathematical calculation on the contents of other cells, the result being inserted in the cell which contains it.

Window

Most business worksheets are quite large, extending beyond the edges of the computer screen. The screen is, in effect, a 'window' into the worksheet. Many spreadsheet packages allow you to set up two or more windows onto your worksheet, so that two or more parts of it can be displayed at the same time on the screen.

Moving around the worksheet

You move the cursor from cell to cell within the spreadsheet window using the arrow keys; when the cursor reaches the edge of the window, any further movement forces the worksheet to scroll past the window. Bigger jumps through the worksheet are possible by using other keys, e.g. by pressing the PgUp or PgDn keys to jump a 'page' (i.e. window) up or down, or by pressing the CTRL key and an arrow key.

Spreadsheet tasks

To set up and use a worksheet, you have to carry out the following tasks.

Designing the worksheet
First of all, you have to design the template. This is a bit like setting up a template for a record-keeping system. You have to:

● decide how the data is to be organized
● insert appropriate column and row labels
● adjust the column widths as necessary
● set the number of decimal places for displaying the data
● program the template, i.e. enter programming statements (formulas) in appropriate cells.

As with a record-keeping system, this is a once-only job, and templates set up for one application can often be used for others, though perhaps with some modification. Public domain templates are available for the most popular spreadsheet packages, and by using these you can set up most standard applications with the minimum of effort.

Adding data
Once the template has been designed, you can enter the data for your application. Any results (totals, averages, etc) will be automatically calculated, using the formulae stored in the results cells.

Altering data
You will often wish to alter numbers previously entered into a cell. For example, if you are using a cash-flow forecast worksheet like that

shown in Figure 8.2, you may wish to find out how changes in certain costs, or sales, affect your future cash flows. You have merely to enter the new figures, and the results are instantly calculated. This kind of activity is very useful for decision-making and planning, because you can easily and quickly investigate the effects of alternative courses of action.

Goal-seeking

Sometimes, you may have certain ideal results which you wish to achieve. You could keep altering the data in your worksheet until what you want is produced in the results cells. Many spreadsheet packages, however, incorporate automatic goal-seeking: you say what you want the results to be, and the spreadsheet will work backwards to the starting-data.

Charting

Most spreadsheet packages will produce various kinds of charts and graphs of the data in the worksheet. Normally, column labels will be used to mark the X-axis, with a selection of data or results being plotted against the Y-axis.

Sorting and searching

Many spreadsheet packages provide limited database facilities such as sorting rows, e.g. into alphabetical order of row labels, or searching for a particular entry.

Spreadsheets and databases compared

Some tasks can be carried out using either a spreadsheet or a database package. For example, you could keep your personal accounts on either. However, there are important differences in the two types of package:

- database packages have sophisticated data retrieval and reporting facilities which are not normally found in spreadsheets
- a spreadsheet provides a more flexible working environment, for it is not limited to the kind of record structures described in the last chapter; for example, a row does not have to be a record, but can be programmed to show totals, averages, or other results.

So when should you use a spreadsheet, and when a database? Spreadsheets are particularly good for handling numerical data and calculating results, and so they are appropriate for many financial and other numerical/calculating applications. Database packages are more appropriate for conventional record-keeping tasks where the main requirement is to retrieve information and produce transaction documents and reports.

Spreadsheet applications

Spreadsheet applications fall into two broad areas, managerial and clerical:

- Managerial applications are those that support the kinds of task that managers have to carry out, in particular decision-making and planning tasks. As mentioned above, spreadsheets enable you easily and quickly to investigate the effects of alternative courses of action. Cash-flow forecasting is a favourite managerial application, and others include profit forecasting, investment appraisal, manpower planning and statistical analyses.
- Clerical applications are those that support bookkeeping and other office tasks that are normally carried out by clerks.

Activity

Use a spreadheet package to set up a template for the cash-flow forecast shown in Figure 8.2, including the formulae that are required. Then enter the data, and try out the effects of altering some of the income and expenditure figures and recalculating the results. Save your work. (Note: if you require help with the formulae, turn to Figure 8.7 at the end of this chapter.)

Business graphics and presentations

Introduction to business and presentation graphics

Business graphics covers a range of software for producing:

- charts and graphs of numerical data, either keyed in or imported from a worksheet

- drawings such as room layouts, diagrams of electrical circuits, or the diagrams used in this book
- notices and overhead projector transparencies using a range of typestyles and typesizes.

Examples of this kind of software include GEM Draw, GEM Chart, and GEM Wordchart, supplied for PCs, Atari STs, and other computers which are able to run GEM. Most spreadsheet packages and most integrated packages also incorporate graphics capabilities enabling you to produce simple bar charts, pie charts, or line graphs of the data contained in worksheets.

I shall restrict my comments here to charting and graphing software. Drawing software is a simple version of the computer-aided design software described in the next chapter.

Charting concepts

Charting concepts that you need to know are *bar chart*, *pie chart*, *XY graph*, *title*, *label*, and *legend*.

Bar chart

An example of a bar chart is shown in Figure 8.3. You use this type of chart when you wish to compare two or three sets of numerical data and to show their trend. In the figure, the data is the monthly income, expenses, and cash balance from the cash-flow forecast example given in the last section.

Pie chart

A pie chart for the cash-flow forecast example is shown in Figure 8.4. You use this type of chart to compare a number of individual items of numerical data.

XY graph

An example of an XY graph is shown in Figure 8.5, in which the monthly sales in the cash-flow example is compared with the corresponding wages. You use this type of chart to compare one set of numerical data against another.

Titles, labels, and legends

To make your charts easy to read, they should always have meaningful titles, the axes should normally be labelled, and a legend

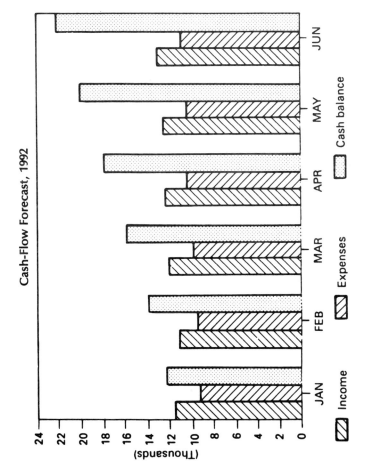

Figure 8.3 Bar chart for cash-flow forecast worksheet

or key should be provided to distinguish the various data ranges. In Figure 8.3, for example, the title is *Cash-Flow Forecast, 1992*, the vertical axis is labelled in thousands of pounds and the horizontal axis is labelled in months, and the legends or keys indicate which bars measure monthly income, which measure monthly expenses, and which measure monthly cash balances.

Charting tasks

Since you normally use spreadsheet software to handle numerical data, it makes sense to use the spreadsheet's charting facilities for presenting that data. In which case, producing a chart is very simple and involves the following tasks.

Select data for charting

Lotus 1-2-3 and other spreadsheet packages allow you to select ranges of data (i.e. sections of a row or column) for charting. So you can pick out the significant parts of your worksheet for displaying and analysing in this way. Normally, you will want to look at calculated results, such as totals, and you can if you wish view a selection of results on the same graph. Figure 8.3 is an example of this.

Enter titles and legends

Most spreadsheet packages allow you to enter titles, legends, other explanatory details.

Charting applications

Charts and graphs are a very useful and powerful way of comparing sets of figures and showing trends in data. They are therefore an effective means of analysing and communicating numerical information, and they are widely used in reports and presentations.

Activity

Use your spreadsheet package to produce charts like those shown in Figures 8.3 to 8.5 from the worksheet you constructed in the last activity.

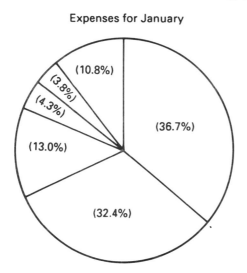

Expenses for January

Figure 8.4 Pie chart produced on Lotus 1-2-3

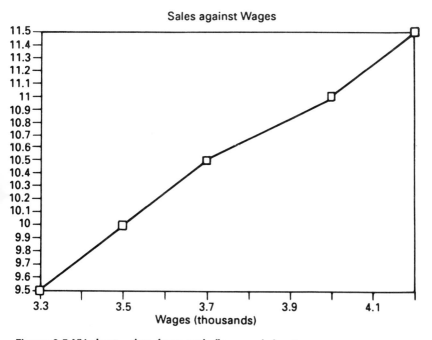

Sales against Wages

Wages (thousands)

Figure 8.5 XY chart – data from cash-flow worksheet

209

Word processing and desktop publishing

Word processing (WP) software aims to make the task of creating and editing text as easy and powerful as possible. In the past, WP packages did not allow you to use a variety of fonts (typestyles) or to incorporate graphics into your documents. Desktop publishing (DTP) software, in contrast, provides very weak word processing facilities, for it assumes that you will create your text using a WP package, but it does allow you to use a wide range of fonts, to control exactly the layout of your material on the page, and to include graphics.

In recent years, however, this distinction between WP and DTP has become less pronounced. Most modern WP packages now allow you to use a variety of fonts, and some will allow you to incorporate graphics in your documents. At the same time, DTP packages are improving their WP features. Nevertheless, at the time of writing the two types of software are quite different, and it is still appropriate to deal with them separately.

Word processing concepts

The main WP concepts are *outline, edit, window, text enhancement, WYSIWYG, page definition, style sheet, block operation, glossary,* and *mailmerge*.

Outline

An *outline* is the skeleton structure of a document, often just a list of headings, subheadings, and sub–subheadings. Outline software exists which enables you to draw up such a list, and then juggle the items around at will and add notes, a sort of 'ideas organizer'. Once you have outlined your document, you can start to fill in the text under the headings and subheadings.

Some word processors incorporate outlining facilities, allowing you to 'collapse' text under headings, so that it disappears from view on the screen. You can then see the structure of your document more clearly, and shuffle headings (with the hidden text) around if you wish to change the order.

Edit

Editing refers to the process of entering and amending text. Because this takes place electronically, avoiding the laborious need to correct documents or retype pages, word processing has revolutionized the writing process.

Window

As with spreadsheets, the screen is a window into the document you are editing. You can move around the window using the arrow keys, larger jumps being possible by pressing, say, the CTRL key and an arrow key. When the cursor reaches the edge of the screen, further movements cause the document to scroll.

Some WP software allows you to create two or more windows on the screen, so that you see two parts of a document at the same time, or view two different documents. You can then easily copy or move text between the two parts of the document.

Text enhancement

This refers to special effects such as emboldening or underlining, or selecting special founts. You enhance individual characters or words in your document by positioning the cursor on them and pressing a function key or the ALT key and a character key – the process varies from package to package. Some WP packages show these effects on the screen exactly as they will appear on paper, so that italics, for example, actually look that way. Other packages are only able to highlight or colour the characters that have been enhanced. How these effects will actually come out on paper depends on the printer you are using.

WYSIWYG

This stands for what you see is what you get. In other words, what's on the screen shows what the document will look like when printed. Most modern WP packages are WYSIWYG so far as the organization of the text is concerned: they show where lines end, the spaces between paragraphs, where the page breaks are, and so on. However, few are WYSIWYG to the extent that they show both this and how the various text enhancements will look.

Page definition

This refers to the line length, margin size, number of lines per page, and other page formatting that you have set up for your document.

WYSIWYG word processors show on the screen how the page definition affects the appearance of the document.

When you create a new document, your WP package will provide a default page definition, with the line lengths etc set up already. If you want your document formatted differently, you can easily change the settings. Many packages also allow you to decide the defaults, so that most of your documents are automatically formatted the way you want them.

Style sheet

Besides the overall page definition, some word processors enable you to set other aspects of layout style, such as indenting the first line of paragraphs. You can prepare a variety of page definitions and styles for different types of document, and save these as *style sheets*. Then, when you create a document, you can attach the appropriate style sheet to it so that the pre-defined style is automatically applied.

Block operation

This refers to the process of deleting, moving, or copying a complete block of text, such as several sentences or paragraphs. The process involves marking the start and the end of the block in some way, then pressing a special key.

Glossary

Many organizations often use identical paragraphs or other sections of text time and time again in many documents. An obvious example is a solicitor's office, producing legal documents for house conveyancing and other transactions. It makes sense to store all these sections of text on disk and insert them as required in documents. Such stored paragraphs and sections of text are called *glossaries*, and some word processors incorporate a special facility to handle them.

Mailmerge

This refers to the process of merging a document with data in a database, in order to print a number of personalized letters. A typical application is inserting automatically in a standard letter the names and addresses of people on a mailing-list – the sort of thing *Reader's Digest* does for its mailshots.

Word processing tasks

Producing a document using a word processing package involves a number of possible operations. Here's a fairly comprehensive list; often you won't use them all.

Outline your document

If you are creating a long and complex document, such as a report, it is helpful to produce an outline of it first. I find drawing up an outline on paper a tedious and untidy process, as I keep wanting to make changes. The best way is to use outlining software on the computer, an excellent public domain (shareware) package for the PC being *PC-Outline*. Grandview, the package I normally use for word processing, is primarily an outliner which includes the standard range of word processing facilities.

Create your document

Once your outline is complete, you can start word processing your document. In theory, you could write the sections of your document in any order, selecting outline headings to work on at will. In practice, most people find it best to start at the beginning and work through to the end, perhaps adding ideas under outline headings as they come to mind. As you create your masterpiece your ideas will mature and your emphases alter, and you will want to modify the outline somewhat; this becomes difficult to do if you start by creating sections lying in the middle of your document.

As mentioned already, when you start a new document your word processor will provide you with a default page definition (line length etc). If you wish to alter this page definition for the current document, you can do so at any time.

Edit your document

As you work on your document, you will want to make changes, and word processing packages provide many powerful tools to help with this. These tools include the following:

● Easy *deleting* facilities, so that you can quickly move to the offending section of text, and delete it character by character, or word by word, or by marking the whole block for deletion.

- *Undo* facilities, so that you can restore text that you have deleted in error. You can also use this facility to move text: you delete the text, move the cursor to the spot where you want it put, and press the undo key.
- *Moving* and *copying* facilities, to move or copy blocks of text within your documents.
- *Merge* facilities, to incorporate standard paragraphs, addresses, and other textual material stored on disk into your document. The process of compiling a document by merging a number of existing pieces of text is called *boilerplating*.
- *Search and replace* facilities, which will automatically search for a word (or words, or part of a word), and, if required, replace it by another. You can ask the computer automatically to replace the word *globally*, i.e. throughout the document, or you can check each occurrence of the word before allowing it to be replaced.
- *Spelling check* facilities, using an electronic dictionary stored on disk, which enable you to check the spelling of an individual word (which you select by moving the cursor to it), or all words throughout the document. If a word does not match what's in the dictionary, the computer highlights it and displays a list of possible replacements on the screen. Most electronic dictionaries are quite general-purpose, and so many allow you to add additional words, and correct existing ones, facilities which are particularly useful if you write technical reports, or if you wish to spell words such as *color* with a *u* — most dictionaries are generated in America!
- Some word processors also provide an electronic *thesaurus*, which will, on request, display a list of words with a meaning similar to the word lying at the cursor. This may help you to improve your style by replacing complex words by simpler or more appropriate ones, or by adding more variety to your choice of words.
- *Word count* facilities, so that as you work on your document you can check whether the length is on target, and make cuts or add more material if it is not.

Check your style

When you have finished your document, you can, if you wish, test its readability using style-checking software. This will perform a number of tests, such as:

- determining the complexity of your sentence structure, by calculating the average number of words and the average number of clauses per sentence
- determining the complexity of the words used, by calculating the percentage of words with three or more syllables
- checking the amount of jargon in your text
- checking the amount of variety in your text
- comparing impersonal words like *its* and *their* with personal words like *your* and *yours* to determine the personal tone of the text.

When it has checked the document, the software will produce a report giving readability index, a jargon index, sentence structure recommendations, and so on. The most lucid style will normally rate a reading age of around 14, with an average sentence length of 18 to 20 words. Some style-checking software will also give you detailed comments on individual sentences, such as those that are too long.

Print your document
Once you have got your document the way you want it, you will want to print it. Word processors generally provide a number of print options, including:

- a choice of single- or double-line spacing
- the ability to justify the text (i.e. line up the right-hand edges of lines as is done in this book) by inserting larger spaces between words or letters
- the ability to insert *headers* at the top or *footers* at the bottom of each page (such as the chapter name) and to number the pages
- the ability to print the text in two or more columns down the page.

Produce mailmerged documents
Most WP packages provide mailmerge facilities, so that data from a database can be incorporated in a document when it is printed. With Q&A, the package that I use, all you do is enter the field labels in your document, distinguishing them from the rest of your text by enclosing them between asterisks. When you print the document, you specify the name of the database file, and which records from the file are to be used. Q&A then prints repeated copies of the letter, one for each record, with the data from that record entered in place of the asterisked field names.

Import or export files

You may wish to include in your document material produced on other packages. Most software provides facilities to export data or text produced in them, i.e. to save the data or text in files that conform to a universally recognized format. Such formats include ASCII for text, DIF (document interchange format) for data, as well as the *dBase II* and *Lotus 1-2-3* formats. Once in that standard format, the files can be imported into other software.

When a word processed document is exported as an ASCII file, all the special characters that produce text enhancements and other formatting are stripped out, leaving the bare text.

WP applications

Word processing has a large number of applications, and these are increasing all the time as the power of WP packages improves and starts to incorporate DTP capabilities. The obvious applications are:

- notes
- letters
- memos
- reports
- books.

Desktop publishing

At a primitive level, any word processor can be used as a desktop publishing (DTP) system. You can design a form or a simple magazine using one, and print it out on a daisy-wheel printer for use as a master for offset litho or photocopying. The problem is that you cannot produce the variety of founts or the pictures and other graphics that are possible with conventional typesetting.

The advent of fairly low-cost laser printers in 1984–1985 brought typesetting just about within the reach of the ordinary microcomputer user. These devices can print any kind of text or graphics effects, a capability that was not lost on the bright boys at Apple Computers. Together with a company called Adobe, they brought out the *Postscript* page description language, a piece of software that enabled laser printers to produce typesetting founts. Another company called Aldus brought out *PageMaker*, software that enabled Apple Macintosh users to *make up* pages on the screen, i.e. insert text and graphics material and organize its layout ready for printing. With this, the DTP revolution was born.

There are, today, a variety of page make-up packages, running not only on the Macintosh but on other computers as well. The PC is particularly well supported, with a good version of PageMaker as well as *Ventura* and other packages, and it now rivals the Macintosh as a DTP workstation.

DTP and typesetting compared

The production of books, magazines, and other published material by conventional typesetting involves the following steps:

1 authoring the original material, often using a WP package
2 editing the author's work, and annotating it with instructions to the typesetters on the founts to be used and the layout of the material
3 typesetting the material, i.e. keying it into the typesetting equipment or transferring it electronically from the author's disks, laying it out on the screen, inserting control codes for various founts, leaving spaces for pictures and diagrams, and printing the masters
4 pasting onto the master the pictures and diagrams
5 printing the final copies using an offset-litho printer.

With desktop publishing, steps 1 to 4 can all be done on the same system. The author's original material is imported into a page make-up package, where it can be laid out on the screen, merged electronically with any pictures and graphics, and have suitable founts inserted. Once the page is right, it can be printed on a laser printer, ready for the offset litho.

The advantages of using DTP rather than traditional typesetting are:

● the publication remains under your complete control
● you can try out different designs and founts, and see their effects immediately
● you can produce the final result much more quickly
● by eliminating the typesetter you can cut costs.

Furthermore, once word processors with full DTP facilities appear (or DTP packages with full word processing facilities appear), the authoring and the page make-up can be done on the same system, and, if required, at the same time.

Personal productivity software

Personal productivity software helps you organize and execute your own work. It replaces the diaries, calendars, calculators, notepads, and other desktop accessories used by office workers, and so it is sometimes referred to as *desktop accessory software.*

Some personal productivity software, such as Sidekick Plus and PC Tools, aims to encompass all or most of these desktop accessories within a single package. Often, this software is RAM-resident, meaning that it remains in the computer's memory while you are running another application, ready to spring to life on the screen at the touch of a key.

To illustrate the value of Sidekick Plus and similar RAM-resident products, suppose you are using an application (such as a database, spreadsheet, or word processor), and you need to do something such as looking up a phone number, making a diary entry, or performing a calculation. You don't have to quit your application in order to run your desk accessory software, instead you press the key that calls up the desk accessory onto the screen, look up the information or make the entry, then press another key to return to your application at the point where you left it.

This kind of facility has obvious benefits for the office worker, making the computer a very flexible information handling device.

Ideas organizers

An ideas organizer, or 'outliner' as it is normally called, is software that enables you to organize entries – which might be tasks, topics, names, or other textual information – into a hierarchical list of headlines. Sidekick Plus includes an outlining module, and PC-Outline and GrandView are excellent outliners which can also be used in RAM-resident mode.

I produced the outline of this book using GrandView (which is not only an excellent outliner but also a good class word processor). The chapter titles were the main headlines; major topics within chapters were subheadlines, which were broken down into more detailed sub-subheadlines. The computer allows you to easily shuffle the headlines around, promote subheadlines to higher levels or demote headlines to lower levels, divide headlines in two or combine separate headlines into one, very quickly and easily.

Most outliners also allow you to collapse (i.e. hide) low-level headlines, so that you can get an instant overview of your main headlines, and immediately expand them again when you want a more detailed view. You can insert text below any headline, which might be a few notes or a substantial document. You can collapse this text, so that it does not get in the way of the rest of the outline, and you can instantly expand it again.

Many outliners allow you to use a variety of labelling styles. For example, major headlines could be labelled I, II, III, etc., subheadlines could be labelled A, B, C, etc., sub-subheadlines could be labelled 1, 2, 3, . . . , and so on. Or you could, if you wished, have no labels at all.

The kinds of tasks you can use outliners for are:

● Developing the outline of a report or a task. You can enter major headlines, then break these down into subheadlines, insert additional headlines or subheadlines at any time, and easily rearrange the outline until you have marshalled your thoughts into order.

● Keeping a file of names, addresses, and telephone numbers. In this file, individual's names might be the main headlines, with the addresses and phone numbers forming subsidiary text. Normally, you will collapse this text, so that only a list of names is visible. New names and addresses can be added at any time, the list can be sorted into alphabetical order (using the outliner's sort facility), and individual names can be quickly located using the search facility.

● Maintaining a 'to-do' list for tasks that are not tied to a particular time and so do not fit into your diary. For this application you will probably have two main headlines, namely 'To do' and 'Done'. New tasks are added under the first headline, and tasks which have been completed are moved from the first headline to the second.

Assignment 8

In your role as summer camp organizer, you wish to create a worksheet which acts as a computerized cash analysis book, by:
a recording all items of income and expenditure under appropriate headings, and

	INCOME				EXPENDITURE			
DATE	Fees	. . .	. . .	. . .	Food	. . .	. . .	. . .	. . .

Figure 8.6 Template outline for Assignment 8

b producing automatically the totals under each heading and the cash balance.

In this worksheet, each transaction, whether an item of income or expenditure, occupies a row. Figure 8.6 shows what the design of a cash analysis page for these accounts might look like in a manual system. The headings on the income side might include fees received from members, sales, and gifts, and expenditure headings might include food, transport, hiring charges, etc.

For this assignment you are required to create the template for this worksheet using a spreadsheet package, enter some test data, and produce from it suitable charts for presenting the camp accounts. You should then write a short report on the accounts for presenting to the youth club committee, incorporating into it the worksheet and the charts. If you have suitable software, you should import both the worksheet and the charts into your word-processed document so that they can be combined electronically instead of being manually pasted up.

Recap

● The term *office automation* is used to describe the application of the computer and related devices to the work of the office. Office automation has followed from the development of the low-cost microcomputer, which can be economically applied to the varied jobs of managers and secretaries.

Cash-flow forecast for Pine Workshop, Jan–June 1992

	JAN	FEB	MAR	APR
INCOME				
Sales				
Other				
Total	+B5+B6	+C5+C6	+D5+D6	+E5+E6
EXPENSES				
Wages				
Stock				
Rent				
Rates				
Fuel				
Other				
Total	@SUM(B10..B15)	@SUM(C10..C15)	@SUM(D10..D15)	@SUM(E10..E15)
B/F	+B20	+C20	+D20	
BALANCE	+B8–B17+B19	+C8–C17+C19	+D8–D17+D19	+E8–E17+E19

Figure 8.7 Formulae for cash-flow forecast worksheet

221

- Office automation increases the *productivity* of office workers, it improves the *accuracy* of the work, and it results in more *management information*, produced more quickly.
- Office automation hardware can include *stand-alone, networked,* and *multi-user* computers, as well as a variety of *related equipment* such as scanners and laser printers. It will, ultimately, result in a considerable reduction in the amount of paper used in offices.
- The main types of office automation software are *database, spreadsheet, graphics, word processing* and *desktop publishing, communications,* and *diary systems and other personal productivity tools.*
- The main record-keeping concepts are *data, file, record, field,* and *template.* The main record-keeping tasks are *designing the file, adding and deleting records, updating records, validating data, searching records, sorting records, calculating,* and *reporting.*
- The main spreadsheet concepts are the same as for record keeping, with the addition of *column, row, cell, formula,* and *window.* The main spreadsheet tasks are *designing the worksheet, adding data, altering data, goal-seeking, charting,* and *sorting and searching.*
- The business graphics concepts are *bar chart, pie chart, XY graph, title,* and *legend.* The main tasks are *selecting data for charting,* and entering *titles and legends.*
- The main word processing concepts are *outline, edit, window, text enhancement, WYSIWYG, page definition, style sheet, block operation, glossary,* and *mailmerge.* The main tasks are *outlining the document, creating the document, editing the document, checking the style, printing the document, producing mailmerged documents,* and *importing or exporting files.*
- Desktop publishing software enables you to perform conventional typesetting tasks on the computer screen, including laying it out, selecting suitable founts, inserting pictures and other graphics. When fed to a laser printer, the final result can be a professional-looking brochure or other document.
- Personal productivity software helps you organize your work, replacing diaries, calculators, notepads, and other desktop accessories. Particularly useful are ideas organizers or *outliners,* which allow you to organize entries into a hierarchical list of headlines, which can then be easily and rapidly reorganized.

Answers to questions

1 Work can be produced more quickly, and more accurately. More information can be produced on the membership, if required, from the membership data. Letters and other output can look better, depending on the quality of printer used, and good-looking graphics can be produced. The increased productivity should result in more time being available for other activities, so that your job becomes better and more productive.
2 Five are: fax, modem, telephone, scanner, laser printer.

9: IT in manufacturing

Objectives

After reading this chapter, you should be able to:
- outline the main steps involved in the manufacturing process, including the initial product planning and design, production planning, and production
- explain the use of data processing and expert systems to aid the initial product planning and the day-to-day task of production planning
- describe how computers can aid the design process by the use of computer-aided design software
- describe how computers can aid the manufacturing process by the use of CNC machines, robots, and flexible manufacturing systems.

Scenario

Business applications of IT extend far beyond word processing, record keeping, and the other office tasks described in Chapter 8. Computers are now widely used for product design and to control all aspects of the manufacturing process.

We are now moving into the era of the *integrated factory*, in which office and factory systems are linked in the way indicated in Figure 9.1 and explained in the next section. Product design, customer orders, and stock-holding information are fed electronically from the office to the factory, which automatically produces the batches of parts and finished goods. The factory in its turn feed production information such as materials usage back via the electronic networks to the office, where stock adjustment, costing and other tasks are carried-out.

The main steps in the manufacturing process

In outline, the main steps in the manufacturing process are as follows. You should relate this list to the activities shown in Figure 9.1.

1 Plan your products, i.e. decide what to produce and how they should be marketed. This preliminary stage will involve bringing together and studying market research information, analyses of orders received from customers in the past, and analyses of production costs, as well as information on relevant technological advances and innovations.

2 Design your products, using the expertise of the drawing–office and other related departments.

3 Receive customers' orders, and from them produce (a) the sales documentation (including invoices) and (b) the production plans for the period ahead to produce the required quantities of parts and finished goods. Note that (b) involves drawing up a production schedule (or timetable) of jobs to be done, and loading (or distributing) the jobs among the various sections and machines.

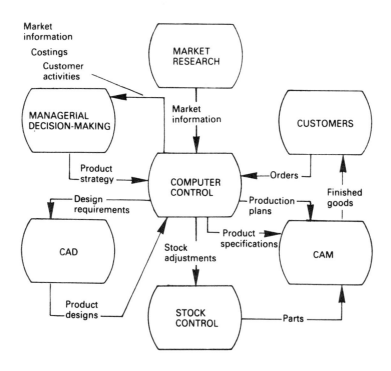

Figure 9.1 Schematic of the integrated factory

4 Pass your design data and production plans to the manufacturing system, so that it can produce the required parts and goods. Raw materials and some parts required for the production process will be drawn from stock.

5 Calculate your manufacturing costs in order to price products, control the manufacturing process, and assist future planning.

6 Despatch the goods and invoices to customers.

In a modern manufacturing business, the computer is involved in all these stages, as illustrated in Figure 9.2. The system shown in that figure are listed below and described in more detail in the next sections.

● *Data processing* (DP). The data processing system is used to process customer orders, stock receipts and issues, purchases, and financial information. From it, production plans, sales documentation, stock records, and other essential manufacturing and sales information can be produced.

● *Expert systems* Although not widely used at present, expert systems are beginning to appear in business, and can aid the product planning and other decision making.

● *Computer-aided design* (CAD). This can greatly increase the productivity of the drawing–office, and in modern factories the CAD system can be linked to the CAM system, so that the designs are directly input to the manufacturing process.

● *Computer-aided manufacture* (CAM). This refers to the use of computers to control the manufacturing process, mainly by controlling the settings of tools and the way they are used in CNC (*computer numerically controlled*) machines and other automatic manufacturing devices.

Data processing systems

Unlike office automation systems (which are to do with the highly variable and low-volume activities of the secretary, administrator, and manager), *data processing* systems deal with the high-volume routine tasks traditionally associated with clerical activities in the organization. These include processing data on the sales, purchases, stock, and financial transactions that take place in the organization. Because of the high volume of work, DP systems are normally based on mini or mainframe computers.

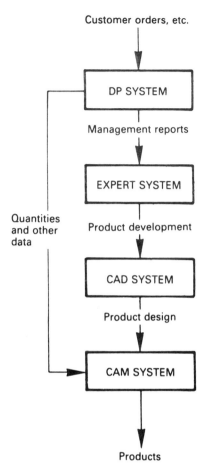

Figure 9.2 The main computer-based systems in a manufacturing business

There are two main ways of organizing data processing: *batch processing* and *real-time processing*. In batch processing, the data is dealt with in batches according to a fixed timetable, with the result that figures held on the computer may be several hours out-of-date. In real-time processing the data is dealt with immediately on input (as is the case in personal computer systems), with the result that up-to-date figures are always available.

227

Batch processing is normally associated with centralized data entry and output facilities, and requires less powerful computers with fewer terminals. Real-time processing is a more expensive option, as it makes much greater demands on the central computer, and terminals must be located throughout the various user departments so that staff can constantly access data. Real-time processing has obvious advantages over batch processing, and with continually reducing computing costs it is becoming the norm.

A typical DP application

A typical data processing application – sales order processing in this example – involves the following steps:

1 Details of the transactions are keyed into the computer, either in batches in a central data processing facility or, in the case of real-time processing, as they arise via terminals in the sales department
2 In the case of batch processing, the transaction data is held on a *transaction file* – a sales transaction file in this case. Later on, the main sales file, or *master file*, is updated with the latest batches of data held on the transaction file. This involves running an update program which accesses both files at the same time. In the case of real-time processing, the data is inserted directly into the sales master file when it is keyed in
3 *Transaction documents*, such as invoices and delivery notes, are produced automatically by the computer from the data held on the master file. The information required by the production plan (see the left-hand arrowed line in Figure 9.2) is also produced from this data.
4 *Management reports* are produced periodically which summarize data held on the master file. In the case of the sales master file, one management report might give the total sales of each type of product and show how the sales are growing (or declining) from month to month. These reports help managers to make decisions by indicating how to develop the product range, what levels of stock to hold, and so on.

Each record in a sales master file relates to one product sold by the company. The fields used in a typical sales master file are listed and described in Figure 9.3.

Field	Description	Field type	Field length
Stock number (e.g. WID234-010)	A code uniquely identifying this part	Alphanumeric	10
Stock description (e.g. SILVER-WIDGETS – BOX OF 10)	The description of this stock item	Alphanumeric	30
Product group (e.g. COMM, this stands for COMponents Misc.)	The code of the broad product category into which this stock item falls	Alphanumeric	4
Last supplier (e.g. 123)	The code of the supplier from whom this item was last purchased	Numeric	3
Cost price (e.g. 50p. This will be written 00000050)	The cost value of this item	Numeric	8 (££££££pp)
Selling price (e.g. £1.25)	The price at which this item is sold	Numeric	8 (££££££pp)
Quantity in stock (e.g. 10)	The quantity currently in the warehouse	Numeric	6
Quantity ordered (e.g. 20)	The number of units required to fill existing sales orders	Numeric	6
Quantity allocated (e.g. 5)	The number of units earmarked against specific orders	Numeric	6

Figure 9.3 Design of a sales master file

Other DP applications

The sales master file will, of course, be just one of a number of master files held on the organization's data processing system. Others include:

- the purchases file, containing records of orders placed with suppliers
- the stock file, containing details of stock and records of stock movements

- the customer file, containing customer details and records of purchases and payments
- the supplier file, containing supplier details and records of payments made
- the employee file, containing employee details.

In a large DP system, all these files may be linked, so that entries made in the sales file, for example, can be used automatically to update the customer file. In the case of an integrated factory, the DP system will be linked to the manufacturing systems, so that customer orders are automatically translated into instructions for the computer–controlled manufacturing process.

Question

1 In the above section, I listed the steps involved in a sales order processing procedure. Now it's your turn: assuming real-time processing, jot down the steps you think might be involved in the purchasing procedure.

To help you, a single record on a purchases file will contain details of a product regularly purchased by your company. Besides the product name and part number, it will contain details of alternative suppliers with the prices as well as records of past purchases, so that the purchasing department can select suitable suppliers. It will also record goods received, so that invoices from suppliers can be passed for payment. The main transaction document produced by the purchases procedure is the purchase order, which shows the details and prices of goods that you are ordering from the selected supplier. This is sent to the supplier, and from his or her point of view it forms the sales order.

Expert systems

An *expert system* is a sophisticated type of application package which:

- stores, in a *knowledge base*, a large number of facts and rules about a field of knowledge or *domain*
- provides ways of linking these facts and rules so that guidance can be given on questions that might be asked within that domain.

Put simply, it is a way of recording and accessing human knowledge in a particular domain. Expert systems have been developed for several domains, including medicine, geology, chemistry, mathematics, and various aspects of business, including repair and maintenance.

To construct an expert system, people who are experts in the domain have to be interviewed at terminals and their knowledge of the domain – i.e. of the facts and rules contained in it – must be keyed in, using a logic programming language. Examples of simple facts and rules written in one such language (PROLOG) is given in Chapter 4. To make use of the knowledge stored in the system, it is necessary to ask questions in the format required by the language or system.

A language like PROLOG is difficult for inexperienced people to use, and so a front-end or *shell* is normally provided. This is a type of application software running in the logic programming language. It is used both by experts in the domain to set up the knowledge base and to keep it up to date, and by users wishing to interrogate it.

One example of an expert system is *MYCIN*, which is used for the diagnosis and treatment of bacterial infections. To set it up, a number of consultants invested thousands of hours of work in building up the knowledge base. A typical rule contained in that base is:

IF the infection is primary bacteraemia
AND the site of the culture is one of the sterile sites
AND the suspected portal of entry is the gastro–intestinal tract
THEN there is suggestive evidence (0.7) that the identity of the organism is bacteriodes.

Having been set up, MYCIN supports doctors and medical assistants who lack specialist bacteriological knowledge and who would otherwise have to call upon the help of a consultant. One obvious benefit of this is that proper medical care can be given in situations where consultants are simply not available. Another more surprising benefit is that, even in situations where consultants are available, MYCIN may actually give better advice. The reason for this is that it contains the knowledge of a number of consultants, not just one, and so is able to draw on a broad base of knowledge and expertise.

When consulted, MYCIN asks the doctor or medical assistant a number of questions about the patient in order to establish the facts of the case. Examples of such facts are the first three lines of the above rule. To answer the questions, the enquirer may have to carry out certain tests on the patient. When the system has elicited sufficient facts, it draws conclusions based on the rules stored in its knowledge base, and assigns probabilities to those conclusions. In the example above, the assigned probability is 0.7, i.e. 70%.

Organization of expert systems

An expert system consists of three components:

- A *knowledge base*, containing the facts and rules gleaned from human experts
- A piece of software called the *knowledge manager*, which controls the knowledge base. This involves updating the base with new knowledge received from experts, and making inferences from the existing knowledge in order to answer questions. An important part of the knowledge manager's task is to give explanations, when asked, of the reasoning behind the conclusions it draws.
- A *situation model*, containing data on the current situation or case. This is used by the knowledge manager to retrieve the appropriate information from the knowledge base.

Conclusions drawn by the knowledge manager which have proved useful can be 'remembered', i.e. stored in the knowledge base. In this way the system can learn with use, and so become more expert. Being independent of the knowledge base, the knowledge manager created for one expert system can be used for other related systems. For example, the MYCIN knowledge manager is used in the EMYCIN system, which is a medical expert system designed for handling a number of different knowledge bases.

Expert systems for business

In data processing, the first applications to be computerized were payroll and invoicing, the reason being that they are governed by unambiguous rules, procedures, and facts. Later, other more complex applications were computerized, but they, too, had to be reduced to precisely defined rules and facts in a program. Expert systems are no different – they are most easily applied in situations where the rules and facts are unambiguous and where conclusions can be logically drawn and assigned probabilities.

So, like the early data processing systems, expert systems applications in business are those which can most easily be reduced to rules. Typical applications are:

- social security regulations in the DSS, to allow people to obtain advice on their entitlements
- income tax regulations, so that advice can be given on ways to minimize tax liability
- maintenance and repair work, where the steps required to track down faults can be precisely defined for each type of equipment.

Just as data processing systems have been refined and are being applied on microcomputers to the less well-defined office tasks, so expert systems may one day be applied to managerial decision-making skills. At the lower managerial levels, many decisions are fairly routine, and expert systems are likely to be applied here first. Later, we might expect to find them being applied in the boardroom.

Such systems will not replace management, at least in the foreseeable future. Although they contain detailed knowledge on particular domains, they lack the breadth of knowledge and the vision of the human mind, and they cannot apply original powers of thought to arrive at creative solutions to problems. The value of an expert system, at least at the higher management levels, is decision-support rather than decision-making:

- It asks the right questions, and so prompts management into getting the relevant information together as a basis for decision-making
- It holds in its knowledge base a vast amount of facts and rules, and so can offer advice which is relevant to decision-making. One example might be the likely impact of setting up a factory in a certain location: the economies or tax incentives to be gained, the availability of materials and labour, and so on.

Similar advice might be gained by asking human experts; the point of such a system is that these experts are in short supply, and no one of them is likely to have at his or her disposal such a depth of knowledge on a particular topic as may be available in a computer expert system.

Question

2 Data processing systems and expert systems both rely on stored information. In the former, the information is held as data in records and fields, whereas in the latter it is organized as facts and rules. Both, however, can be of value to management in helping it decide what to produce.

From the manager's point of view, the main differences between the two systems are that they are looking at different types of knowledge, and they present their findings in different ways. Explain in detail (i.e. half a page) these two differences.

Computer-aided design

A *computer-aided design* (CAD) package does for drawings what a word processing package does for text. Like WP, CAD enables you to:

- delete, insert, copy, and move things rapidly and easily around on the computer screen
- insert existing material stored on disk – such as drawings of parts and sub-assemblies – into your latest masterpiece, so that you are not constantly re-inventing (or rather re-drawing) the wheel
- format your work, so that it is printed or plotted in the colours, line types and so on, that you require

CAD packages also offer a number of additional and valuable drawing aids, including:

- the computer's equivalent of geometric tools such as the compass, the ruler, the protractor, and arcs
- the computer's equivalent of the nib, that allows you to draw different types and thicknesses of lines
- a grid-locking facility, so that the start and end points of any lines that you draw are locked onto a grid of 'graph paper' points on the screen
- zoom facilities, enabling you to expand any part of your drawing on the screen and thereby work more accurately
- rotating, inverting, and other facilities enabling you to manipulate parts of your drawing in a very flexible way

- scaling facilities, enabling you to type in line lengths, angles, and other dimensions at the keyboard, the computer converting these to the required lines on the screen
- dimensioning facilities, which automatically calculate and display on your drawing the lengths of any lines that you may have drawn.

The keyboard is not a suitable drawing tool, and so CAD systems normally use a mouse or another device which converts hand movements to lines on the screen. The most popular system running on PCs is *Autocad*, which uses the mouse. On the BBC micro the main system is the *Robocom CAD* system, which uses a joystick-like device called a *Bitstik*.

The mouse (and the Bitstik) enable you not only to draw lines quickly and easily, they also allow you to point to and select drawing tools and other facilities from a menu that is normally displayed at the edge of the screen. Figure 9.4 shows the Robocom screen display, with:

- various drawing tools – such as different types of arc, colours, and nibs – across the bottom
- a menu of other facilities down the right-hand side
- the drawing area occupying the rest of the screen.

CAD and productivity

CAD systems can achieve impressive productivity gains in drawing offices, and it is often claimed that a 400% increase in output can be achieved. This does, however, assume that the draftsman is familiar with the CAD system and is using its capabilities to the full.

To give an example of the speed at which an item can be drawn, consider a spoked wheel. To draw this, it is only necessary to draw a single spoke and then rotate it through 360 degrees about the centre point of the wheel, duplicating the spoke say every 15 degrees. The hub and the rim can then be rapidly drawn using the CAD package's electronic compass. Any bolts or other parts can be called up from a library held on disk and inserted as required on the drawing.

To give another example, look at Figure 9.5 which shows an aircraft display panel drawn using the Robocom system. Many of the dials are the same size, so they can be drawn once and copied. Other elements are also common, for example the numbers on the dials, so

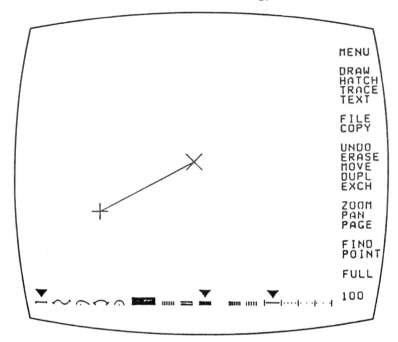

Figure 9.4 The robocom CAD system screen display

they can be treated similarly. Other parts, such as the screw heads and the nuts, can be called up from a library of standard parts held on disk and inserted at the required points in the drawing. The fine detail of the badge at the top of the drawing towards the left can be drawn using the zoom facility. Besides this, the dials can be accurately positioned on the drawing using the grid facility, giving an accuracy that would be impossible using manual methods.

Even greater productivity may be achieved when the CAD system is linked directly to the CAM system, described below. Then, the CAD data can be used directly to control the settings of automatic machines in the factory.

Question

3 Turn to Figure 9.6 and list the sequence of steps that might be used to draw that diagram on a CAD system.

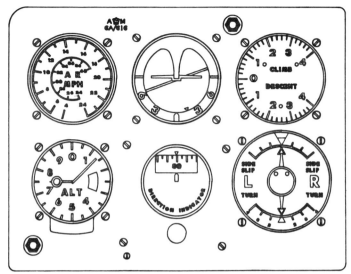

Figure 9.5 Drawing produced using a Robocom system

Activity

If you have access to a CAD package, or else a drawing package such as GEM Draw, spend some time exploring its facilities. Try using it to draw **Figure 9.6.**

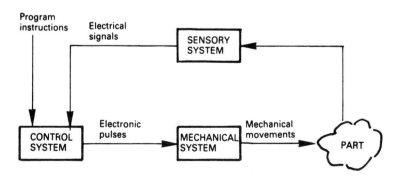

Figure 9.6 Schematic of an 'intelligent' machine

237

Computer-integrated manufacturing

Computer-integrated manufacturing (CIM) covers a range of technologies and techniques that seek to use the power of the computer to ensure that all activities, equipment, and processes in a manufacturing organization work together in the most effective way to achieve its objectives. The word 'integrated' means that CIM is more than merely the piecemeal application of the automated production techniques described later in this chapter – robots, NC machines, automatic materials handling, and so on. A central concern is the flow and the use of information, so that each part of the organization, whether sales, purchasing, warehousing, or production, knows at any point in time exactly what it should be doing in order to be properly integrated into other activities and so optimize overall performance. This means that data has to be processed and passed between the various systems and machines, and so CIM is heavily dependent upon data processing.

The technologies and techniques that are embraced by CIM can be split into four broad areas:

- planning manufacturing
- controlling manufacturing
- executing manufacturing
- integrating manufacturing.

Some of these techniques are described in this chapter. Here's a comprehensive (though not exhaustive) list of them.

Techniques for planning manufacturing

Computer-aided design (CAD)
Computer-aided process planning (CAPP)
Manufacturing resources planning (MRP)
Just-in-time (JIT)
Optimized production technology (OPT)

Techniques for controlling manufacturing

Work-in-progress (WIP) planning and control
Automatic materials handling (AMH)
Quality assurance (QA)
Engineering data management (EDM)

Techniques for executing manufacturing

CNC (computer-numerically-controlled) machines and robotics
Flexible manufacturing systems (FMS)

Techniques for integrating manufacturing

Connectivity issues, including networking standards such as
Manufacturing Automation Protocol (MAP).
   Note also the following terms:

- CAM (computer-aided manufacture) — used to describe a
  combination of CNC machines, robots, and automatic materials handling.
- CAD/CAM – used to describe the linking of CAD to CAM, a
  technique which enables designs created in the drawing office to
  be passed electronically direct to CNC machines and robots in
  the factory, which automatically convert them to parts and
  products.

The evolution of manufacturing technology

The application of computers to manufacturing began around 30
years ago. Since then, there has been a steady evolution in
computer-based factory automation techniques, accompanied by a
gradual progression towards greater levels of integration. This
evolution has, to a large extent, been governed by developments in
computers over the last three decades.

The 1960s

Computers were first applied to manufacturing in the early 1960s.
These were the days of the early batch-processing mainframe
computers, which were suitable for data processing (DP) tasks but
not for controlling factory equipment (see below). Consequently it
was the DP side of manufacturing that was computerized, the
principal technique that we have inherited from that time being
MRP.

The 1970s

Then, in the 1970s, new types of computers came along. Their significance for manufacturing was that they were able to respond instantaneously to data received from sensors. Individual machines, groups of machines, and processes could now be brought under computer control. However, the lack of standards at this time, and the proliferation of differing approaches, meant that these computer-comtrolled devices were not linked together but worked largely independently of each other. This resulted in the so-called 'islands of automation' (see the next paragraph). During the 1970s, the base technologies of modern manufacturing automation were developed, such as computer-numerically-controlled (CNC) machines and robots, computer-based statistical quality control techniques, and computer-aided design.

The term 'islands of automation' has been coined to describe the many different computer-controlled devices within a factory that work with little reference to each other, i.e. with no provision for data to pass between them. One example was the use of computers for statistical quality control – these could rapidly signal deviations in the output of a process outside the accepted tolerance limits, but they could not stop the process for the fault to be rectified. This meant that the overall control and coordination of the process was carried on much as before, i.e. by manual rather than electronic methods.

As indicated above, this lack of communication between automated equipment was due to the lack of agreed standards, rather than being an inherently difficult task. Indeed, while the physical work that lathes and millers (for instance) might do is different, the task of controlling them is actually very similar, using devices called programmable logic controllers (PLCs).

The 1980s

The 1980s was the decade of the personal computer and computer networks. It is the latter that has been particularly significant for manufacturing, for it has enabled many different computers and pieces of equipment to be linked together electronically. ('Connectivity' is the term that's often used to describe this.) This is bringing about the next phase of the evolution in factory automation, namely the setting up of connections between the islands of automation, and between these islands and a supervisory computer. A demonstration of this is the linking of CAD systems to manufacturing systems, so that designs produced in the drawing office are sent electronically to the factory machines, where, with the minimum of human intervention, they are converted into products. This linkage leads to further productivity and performance gains. It also allows the power of the computer to be used to integrate the various processes, ensuring that they work together to optimize the performance of the enterprise as a whole. The term computer-integrated manufacturing (CIM) is specifically applied to this development.

The 1990s

It looks like the 1990s will be the age of telecommunications, resulting in connectivity not just within an organization but between organizations. One example of the trend towards this is the growing number of companies communicating with each other using Electronic Data Interchange (EDI) technology (see page 161). EDI allows standard electronic 'forms' – such as purchase orders or invoices – to be passed between the computers of different organizations, cutting out postal delays and saving storage space and paperwork handling costs.

This type of development will lead to the integration of factory systems with the systems of outside suppliers and customers. Some organizations are already moving in this direction, prompted mainly be the development of just-in-time (JIT) techniques, which aim to cut inventories and improve efficiency by ensuring that supplies of materials and parts arrive at the point of production immediately prior to manufacturing. The successful application of JIT depends partly on the supplier of materials and parts responding rapidly to a customer's requirements, which in turn depends upon manufacturing and distribution systems receiving timely data via EDI from the customer's manufacturing systems. This is best achieved by electronic links between the computers of the two organizations, and from there it is but a short step to arranging that the supplier's factory responds automatically to demands from the customer's factory.

Another result of the development of telecommunications is the concept of the 'global shop floor'. Many organizations have geographically dispersed factories, with different parts of the production process carried out in different countries, and so they need to apply CIM concepts across national frontiers. Groups of machines need to be linked not just to other equipment in their own factory but to equipment in other factories in the organization. The systems that have evolved track work-in-progress (WIP) not just in the individual factory but throughout the entire organization.

The impact of CIM

There are, as yet, no factories which are integrated to the extent that all operations – from order to processing through design and manufacture to distribution – are centrally controlled and coordinated by computer. Indeed, in many cases it is not desirable to aim for such a high level of integration and automation. Where factory automation has been applied, the aim so far has been to integrate some parts only of the enterprise. Here are three examples:

- In one organization, CAD/CAM might be applied. This integrates and automates the design and manufacturing processes, but it impinges only marginally on other areas.
- In another organization, JIT might be applied. This integrates manufacturing and distribution, but has limited impact elsewhere.
- Yet another organization might apply both CAD/CAM and JIT. Although this extends the degree of integration, there are many activities still excluded.

The benefits of factory automation

Organizations which have implemented CIM techniques have benefited in a number of ways. A recent survey commissioned by the DTI and carried out by Benchmark Research revealed the following perceived benefits from CIM:

- increased flexibility in manufacturing operations
- increased productivity

- reduction in lead times
- reduction in costs
- improved product quality.

Creating the integrated factory

To implement CIM, the DP system and the various automated manufacturing systems must be closely tied together by electronic links. There must be a large computer (typically a mainframe) in overall control of these systems, running special software such as the TIME software described in the next section. This same computer may also run the DP system and the various CIM systems, in which case the links between these systems will be purely software links.

The first phase may be to link the CAD system to the CAM system, to create a CAD/CAM system. In this, the product design created on the CAD software is converted by the CAM software to instructions for the factory machines, so that the settings for the machines and the tools used are automatically determined.

In the second phase, the DP system may be tied to the CAD/CAM system to create what's sometimes called an *integrated factory*. In this, the information from customers' orders is used to control the scheduling and loading of work in the factory, so that it automatically produces what's required. As well as this, the DP system is linked to the CAD system, so that it passes to it management reports and market information for use in product design.

These key systems that make up the integrated factory are shown in Figure 9.2. Note that the links that are shown in the figure between these systems take place via the controlling software, as explained in the next section. At present, CAD/CAM is quite widely employed, but few integrated factories exist, apart from some in Japan.

The remaining sections of this chapter describe a range of CIM technologies and techniques, beginning with a brief description of software that can be used to control the integrated factory.

243

Controlling the integrated factory

One example of software for controlling the integrated factory is *TIME*, short for Tandem Integrated Manufacturing Environment. As its name implies, this system is a product of Tandem Computers, and runs on their mainframes.

A schematic of the TIME system is shown in Figure 9.7. It consists of three modules, called *Factory Manager, Document Manager,* and *Device Manager.* These modules perform the following broad tasks:

● The Factory Manager controls the minute-by-minute progress of parts through the factory, to ensure that orders are produced at the right time and to the right specifications. The basis of this control is information on customer orders obtained from the data processing system.
● The Document Manager takes the designs produced by the CAD system and passes them around the factory to the machines that require them, when they require them.
● The Device Manager is really the interface between these two managers and the factory machines. It interprets the information produced by the Factory Manager and the Document Manager

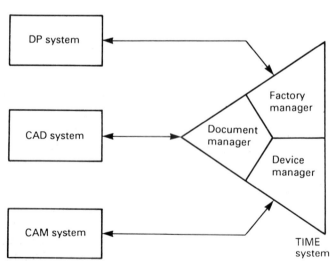

Figure 9.7 Schematic of the TIME system

into the instructions that are passed to the CNC machines, robots, and other factory devices.

The following sections describe two of the main CIM techniques, namely CAM and FMS.

Computer-aided manufacture

Computer-aided manufacture (CAM) refers to the use of computers to control the manufacturing process, primarily by controlling the settings of tools and the way they are used in computer-numerically-controlled (CNC) machines and other automatic devices, and by controlling the deployment of industrial robots. The CAM system uses the production plans produced by the DP system, and the product designs produced by the CAD system, to work out what should be made at what times and on which machines.

To understand what's involved, you should know that factory production typically involves two major processes:

● the machining of parts
● the handling of parts and their assembly.

Today, CNC machines can carry out the first process very efficiently, even for small runs. Operating automatically under software instructions, they can apply various drilling, turning, and cutting devices to the raw material to manufacture an accurately made part.

Robots can carry out the second of these processes, for they can handle materials and feed them to the CNC machines. They can also remove the finished parts and, if necessary, assemble them to make the finished products. Like CNC machines, they can be used economically for small runs. An industrial robot typically consist of a *robot arm* with a clasping device or other tools attached.

Early generations of CNC machines and robots lacked 'intelligence', meaning that they did not have sensory devices enabling them to respond to changes in their environment. In the case of robots, this meant that they would perform the sequence of operations dictated by the controlling software, blindly picking up and manipulating whatever object happened to be placed in the operating position, or, if nothing was there, picking up and manipulating empty space.

Modern generations of CNC machines and robots are equipped with sensors enabling them to identify and locate objects, and so make adjustments to the programmed sequence of operations that they have to perform. In essence, a machine of this type consists of three systems:

● a mechanical system to operate tools or to pick up and manipulate objects; this system may include rotating shafts, drills, and other tools, as well as clasping and other handling devices
● a sensory system to detect what the mechanical system is doing and, in the case of robots, to identify and locate objects; a variety of sensing devices are used, including, for robots, video 'eyes'
● a control system which interprets the information received by the sensory system and uses it to control the mechanical system; this system is normally based on microchips.

In simple terms, the sequence of operations that takes place when one of these machines performs a task is as follows:

● the sensory system converts the position of a part into data in the form of an electrical signal
● the control system compares this with an ideal computed position based on data from the controlling program
● the difference between the two is the 'error', and is represented by tiny digital pulses of electricity
● these pulses are fed to the mechanical system, where they are converted to analogue form, and amplified to the level needed to adjust the positions of the arms and tools.

In a CAM system, a production line consists of CNC machines, robot arms, and materials transfer systems, all under the control of a central computer.

Flexible manufacturing systems

Because modern CNC machines and robots are software-driven, they can be switched from task to task in a very flexible way. Also, production plans can be equally flexible, because they are calculated by the computer data processing system. The combination of the two is *flexible manufacturing systems* (FMS), a term used to describe the ability of modern manufacturing operations to switch rapidly from one product specification to another.

FMS offers great benefits for many types of production:

● Batch production, which accounts for a large part of manufacturing activity, can be automated, with resulting cost and quality benefits.

● Large-scale production is no longer tied to huge production runs of identical products. A car manufacturing plant, for example, can make cars to order without incurring heavy set-up costs. This means that dealers or customers can specify the colours and accessories required, and the quantities, and these can be quickly assembled.

● FMS allows the factory to operate on a just-in-time (JIT) basis, i.e. parts and products can be made at the time that they are required, rather than being made for stock weeks or months ahead. This cuts down greatly on stock-holding costs.

Assignment 9

Referring to published articles as necessary, draw a sketch plan of an integrated factory which makes cars, showing links between the central computer and the various systems, such as those shown in Figure 9.1. Then:

a describe in outline the purposes of each of the systems shown
b list the main items of information that pass between them
c outline the main steps that take place between the receipt of customers' orders and the despatch of the finished goods
d explain the advantages of using flexible manufacturing systems for the production of this type of consumer goods.

Recap

● The main steps in the manufacturing process are *product planning, product design, production planning, production, despatch* and *invoicing*.

● In the modern business, the main computer-based systems used to aid the manufacturing process are *data processing systems, expert systems, computer-aided design systems,* and *computer-aided manufacturing systems*.

- Data processing systems are used for the high-volume routine processing associated with the business's sales, purchases, stock, financial, and other clerical applications. The data will be stored on computer files– such as the sales file, the purchases file, the stock file, the customer file, and the supplier file – each record referring to a single product (in the case of sales, purchases, or stock files), or a single individual or firm (in the case of customer or supplier files).

- A typical data processing application, such as sales order processing, involves the following steps: keying in the transaction data, incorporating it in the appropriate file, printing out transaction documents such as invoices, analysing and summarizing the data for management reports produced to aid decision-making.

- An expert system is a type of application package which stores a large number of *facts* and *rules* about a *domain* of knowledge, and provides ways of linking them so that *advice* can be given on questions asked within that domain. They enable a vast amount of human knowledge to be stored in an easily accessible form. In the future, expert systems are likely to be used to aid managers make business decisions, such as what to produce, and where to produce it.

- Computer-aided design (CAD) software can give a fourfold increase in productivity in the design office, as well as enabling more accurate drawings to be made. Using this software, the draftsman is provided with a range of electronic drawing tools and facilities, including: the computer's equivalent of the *compass*, the *ruler*, the *protractor* and *arcs*; *grid* facilities; *zoom* facilities; *rotating, inverting, moving,* and *copying* facilities; *scaling* facilities; and *dimensioning* facilities.

- Computer-aided manufacture (CAM) refers to the use of computers to control the manufacturing process, mainly by controlling the settings and use of tools in automatic equipment such as CNC machines.

- Flexible manufacturing systems (FMS) take CAM a stage further, by using robots and computer-controlled transfer systems to move parts and materials between processes. FMS not only reduces manufacturing costs, it enables the manufacturer to switch quickly between producing one model and producing another. This makes tiny production runs economical, which reduces stock levels, and it enables the supplier easily to customize goods, which means that the service to the customer is improved.

- In the so-called *integrated factory* all these computer-based systems are linked, so that information relating to customers' orders and product designs is fed electronically to the manufacturing systems, so that the required goods are produced automatically.

Answers to questions

1 The procedures used in the purchasing department will vary somewhat from company to company. A possible sequence of steps is as follows:

● receive from user departments (such as stores) the details of products to be purchased, perhaps on purchase requisition forms or else displayed on a terminal screen

● for each item to be purchased, key in the code number so that the appropriate record from the purchases file appears on the screen, and choose a suitable supplier

● key in the necessary details – such as the supplier number and the quantity to order– so that the purchases file is updated and, at the end of the day, the required purchase orders are printed

● periodically print out management reports, showing e.g. total purchases by product type and by supplier, one purpose of these being to indicate if the company is becoming over-dependent on just one or two suppliers

● later on, when the goods are received, key the details into the purchases file in order to update the purchase records; this information will be used for approving invoices from suppliers for payment.

2 A data processing system is restricted to data on business transactions, such as sales and purchases. It does not deal with information which is external to a business, such as the characteristics of different business locations or the current trends in technology. Expert systems can deal with broader areas of knowledge, but they will not hold detailed data on the organization's transactions.

Data processing systems help management by summarizing the data to show totals and trends – they give an exact quantitative analysis of what's going on in a business and between the business and its suppliers and customers. Expert systems give more qualitative advice, applying a variety of rules to facts which are often non-numerical to come up with an expert opinion.

3 The steps involved in drawing Figure 9.6 might be:

● draw one of the boxes, positioning its corners accurately using the grid facility provided by the package

● copy the box to the two other positions indicated in the drawing

● draw one of the arrow heads, and copy it to the other points, rotating through 90 degrees as necessary

● draw the lines linking the boxes to the arrow heads, again using the grid facility to position them accurately

● turn off the grid facility and draw, freehand, the border of the element labelled *PART*.

Index